FRAGILE
EARTH

FRAGILE EARTH

Collins
An imprint of HarperCollins Publishers
Westerhill Road
Bishopbriggs
Glasgow G64 2QT

First Edition 2011

Printed in Thailand

British Library Cataloguing in Publication Data
A catalogue record for this book is available from the British Library

ISBN 978 0 00 789917 3
Imp 001

All mapping in this book is generated from Collins Bartholomew digital databases.
Collins Bartholomew, the UK's leading independent geographical information supplier,
can provide a digital, custom, and premium mapping service to a variety of markets.
For further information:
Tel: +44 (0) 141 306 3752
e-mail: collinsbartholomew@harpercollins.co.uk

or visit our website at: www.collinsbartholomew.com

Cover image:
Eyjafjallajokull volcano, Iceland
photobucket.com / Existentia

Collins
FRAGILE
EARTH

CONTENTS

IMAGE LOCATIONS

Locations of images found in the book,
and pages on which they first appear.

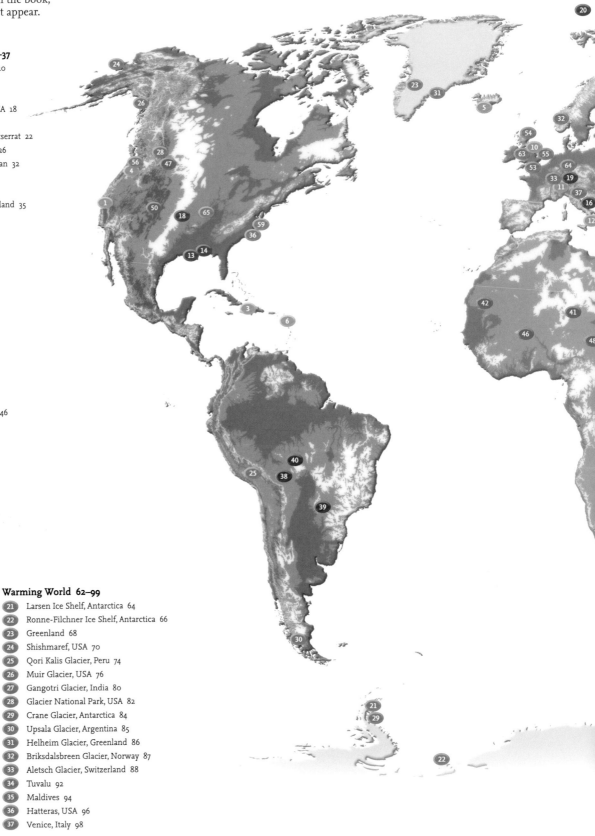

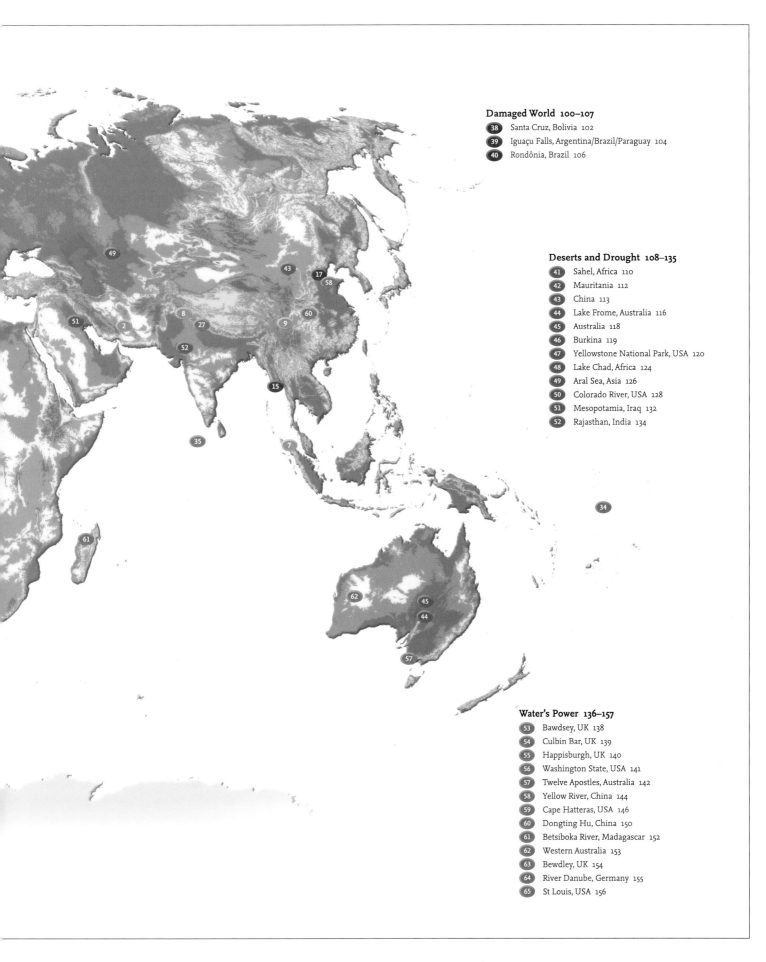

EARTHQUAKES

destructive movements of the Earth's surface due to sudden releases
of energy in the Earth's crust or upper mantle

Hanshin expressway, Kobe, Japan 1995

FERRY BUILDING, SAN FRANCISCO, USA 1906 AND 2006

2006 was the centenary of the great San Francisco earthquake and fire. The top image shows the Ferry Building and its distinctive clocktower which survived the 1906 earthquake. It also survived the 1989 earthquake. The A. Page Brown steel-framed building originally opened in 1898 as a railway and ferry terminal. The lower picture shows it today. It is still a ferry terminal and also a thriving marketplace.

CALIFORNIA STREET, SAN FRANCISCO, USA 19 MAY 1906 AND 23 MARCH 2006

The earthquake and fire of 1906 destroyed buildings but not the overall street pattern of San Francisco. The main building in the top view looking down California Street is the Grace Church, which was subsequently relocated.

The building on this site today is the Ritz Carlton Hotel. The relocated church became the Grace Cathedral, the third largest Episcopalian cathedral in the USA.

BAM CITADEL, IRAN APRIL 1997

The citadel at Bam in Iran is 1000 km (630 miles) southeast of Tehran. It dates back 2000 years and is mainly made of mud bricks, clay, straw, and the trunks of palm trees.

The city was originally founded during the Sassanian period AD 224–637 and its restoration had been ongoing since 1953.

AFTER THE EARTHQUAKE...

On 26 December 2003 an earthquake of magnitude 6.6 struck southeastern Iran killing over 43 000 people and destroying much of the city of Bam. About 60 per cent of the buildings were destroyed. The old quarter of the city and the citadel were severely damaged.

HAITI EARTHQUAKE, LÉOGÂNE 13 JANUARY 2010

On 12 January 2010 an earthquake of magnitude of 7.0 struck Haiti near the town of Léogâne. The effects of this can be seen above in the town where over 80 per cent of all buildings were affected and over 200 000 people were killed. Camps were set up in open spaces such as sports fields and food was distributed with the help of local scouts and guides. Medical facilites were set up close to the local nursing school.

HAITI EARTHQUAKE, PORT-AU-PRINCE 13 JANUARY 2010

In Port-au-Prince most of the historic centre of the city was destroyed. In the centre of the main picture is the Presidential Palace where the upper floor came down on the lower one. The effects can be seen more clearly in the before and after inset images.

There is also much evidence of the destruction of other buildings in the bottom left of the image. Goups of people can be seen in many of the open spaces where they can avoid collapsed buildings, collect food and get medical attention.

VOLCANOES

openings in the Earth's crust from which molten lava, rock fragments,
ash, dust, and gases are ejected

Eyjafjallajökull, Iceland

THE ERUPTION OF MOUNT ST HELENS, USA 18 MAY 1980

On 20 March 1980, after 123 years of inactivity, Mount St Helens awoke when an earthquake of magnitude 4.2 rumbled beneath it. Over the next two months a vast area was pushed outward which became known as 'the bulge'. This was caused by the rise of molten rock within the volcano. On 18 May another earthquake triggered a huge rockslide and a major volcanic eruption as the bulge gave way.

MOUNT ST HELENS BEFORE AND AFTER... 17 MAY 1980 AND 10 SEPTEMBER 1980

During the eruption, 400 m (1300 feet) of the north flank of the mountain collapsed or blew outwards and a plume of ash reached a height of 20–25 km (12–15 miles).

The plume moved eastwards at an average speed of 95 km (60 miles) per hour, felling trees and killing most wildlife and vegetation within a 550 sq km (212 sq mile) area.

BIRTH OF AN ISLAND, SURTSEY, ICELAND NOVEMBER 1963

On 14 November 1963 fishermen observed the beginnings of an undersea eruption. An island was eventually created to a height of 169 m (554 feet) above sea level with an area of 2.5 sq km (0.97 sq miles). This island was named Surtsey after Surtur, the fire-possessing giant of Norse mythology who would set fire to the Earth at the Last Judgment.

NEW ISLAND GROWTH, SURTSEY, ICELAND   1965 AND 2000

Over a period of three and a half years Surtsey erupted and lava flowed. Before the eruption stopped the island was made a nature reserve and travel was restricted to scientists who studied the gradual development of life on this new land. Surtsey is now a favourite resting place for migratory birds and marine wildlife.

A TOWN ENGULFED... PLYMOUTH, MONTSERRAT 1997

Plymouth, the former capital of the British territory of Montserrat in the Caribbean, was buried in volcanic ash as a result of eruptions of the Soufrière Hills volcano several times between 1995 and 1997. The town, which was the island's largest settlement, had to be abandoned and many of the residents moved away from the island and have not returned.

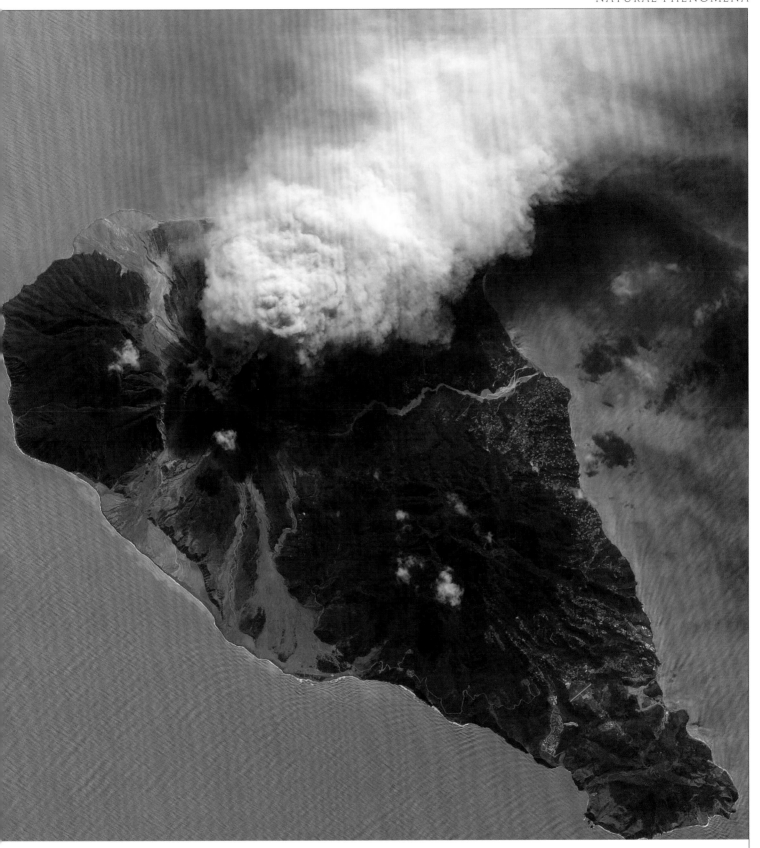

MONTSERRAT 2009

In October 2009 there were earthquakes and ash clouds appeared. These plumes can deposit ash at great distances from the island. Further activity in February 2010 deposited ash on Guadeloupe and Antigua. Although parts of the island remain inhabited and many of the services lost when Plymouth was destroyed have been moved elsewhere, this image shows how vulnerable the remaining population is to another large eruption.

TSUNAMI

large, often destructive, sea waves produced by submarine earthquakes,
subsidence, or volcanic eruptions

Tsunami hazard warning post, Thailand

BANDA ACEH, SUMATRA, INDONESIA 10 JANUARY 2003

Banda Aceh is a provincial capital of Indonesia on the very northern tip of the Indonesian island of Sumatra. The edge of the town is to the top right of this image.

Seen here in a satellite image captured in January 2003, various types of agriculture are being undertaken and there is extensive woodland close to the town.

AFTER THE TSUNAMI... 29 DECEMBER 2004

After the tsunami of 26 December 2004, much of the coast is under water as the surface vegetation and soil has been stripped off by the waves. In the town, buildings have been destroyed and a huge amount of debris has collected in some areas.

Flooding extends well inland, where there is less destruction of property but widespread loss of agricultural land.

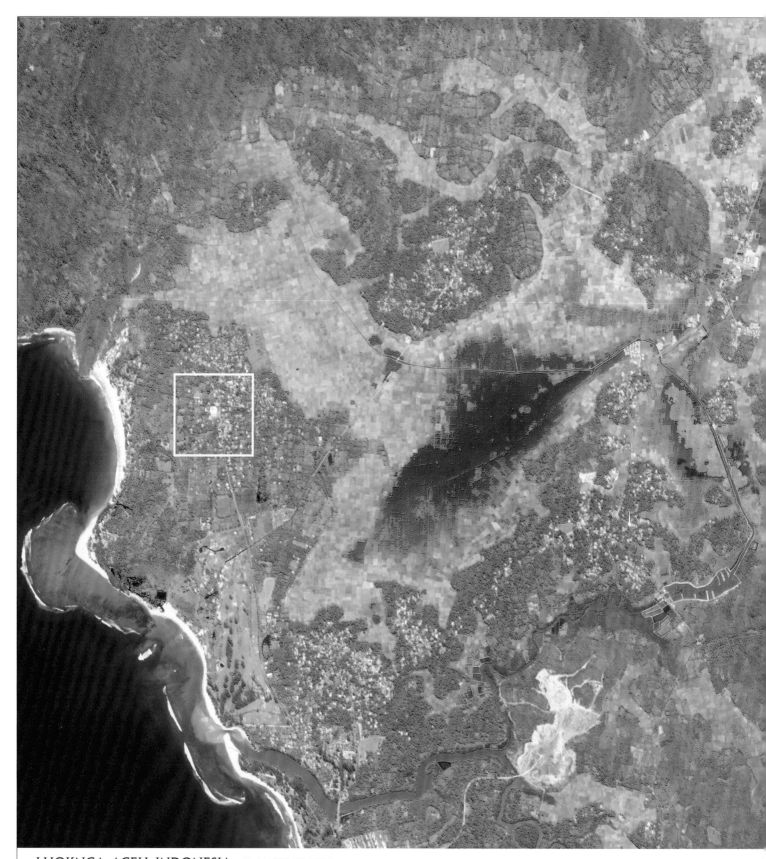

LHOKNGA, ACEH, INDONESIA 10 JANUARY 2003

Captured in January 2003, this satellite image of Lhoknga, near the provincial capital of Banda Aceh, shows lush and well-cultivated land, with woodland and several villages.

The darker area in the centre is water and there are several canals. The coast has sandy beaches, some with barrier islands or reefs protecting them..

TSUNAMI AFTERMATH... 27 DECEMBER 2004

Three days after the tsunami the extent of the destructive force of the waves can be seen. The coastal area has been stripped bare of vegetation and buildings with only the prominent Rahmatullah Lampuuk Mosque remaining. Inland, the low-lying areas are now filled with salt water and it is only the slightly higher level of the roads which keeps them visible.

LANDSLIDES

movements of large masses of rock,
down mountains or cliffs

Landslide destroys a bridge

NEELUM RIVER, PAKISTAN 15 SEPTEMBER 2002 AND 9 OCTOBER 2005

These satellite images show the Neelum river at Makhri just north of Muzaffarabad, before and after the magnitude 7.6 earthquake which struck northern Pakistan on 8 October 2005. Major landslides have blocked the river's usual course, forcing it to change direction. Its water is brown with sediment from many more landslides upriver.

SICHUAN LANDSLIDES, CHINA 19 FEBRUARY 2003 AND 23 MAY 2008

The earthquake that struck Sichuan on 12 May 2008 created devastation in the wider landscape as well as in towns and cities. Many landslides were triggered which caused problems with rescue efforts. This area is around 150 km (90 miles) from the epicentre.

The false colour images show vegetation in red and the later image has many grey patches where bare ground has been exposed by the many landslides heading downslope into the rivers.

HOLBECK HALL HOTEL, SCARBOROUGH, ENGLAND 4 JUNE 1993 AND 5 JUNE 1993

On 3 June 1993, Holbeck Hall Hotel was a four-star establishment standing about 65 m (213 feet) above the sea on the South Cliff, Scarborough on the East Yorkshire coast, UK. It looked out over an expanse of lawn to panoramic views of the North Sea. But by the 6 June, as a result of a massive landslide which took place in four stages, the lawn had disappeared and the ground had collapsed under the whole of the seaward wing of the hotel.

STIEREGG HUT, GRINDELWALD, SWITZERLAND 1 JUNE 2005 AND TWO DAYS LATER

The Stieregg Hut is a restaurant located at 1650 m (5413 feet) near Grindelwald in Switzerland. There was a massive landslide on Sunday 1 June 2005 which left the hut delicately positioned. Fortunately, the hut had been evacuated before the start of the summer season. Almost immediately there was another landslide and by 3 June the hut was precariously balanced, hanging over the edge of a very long and steep drop.

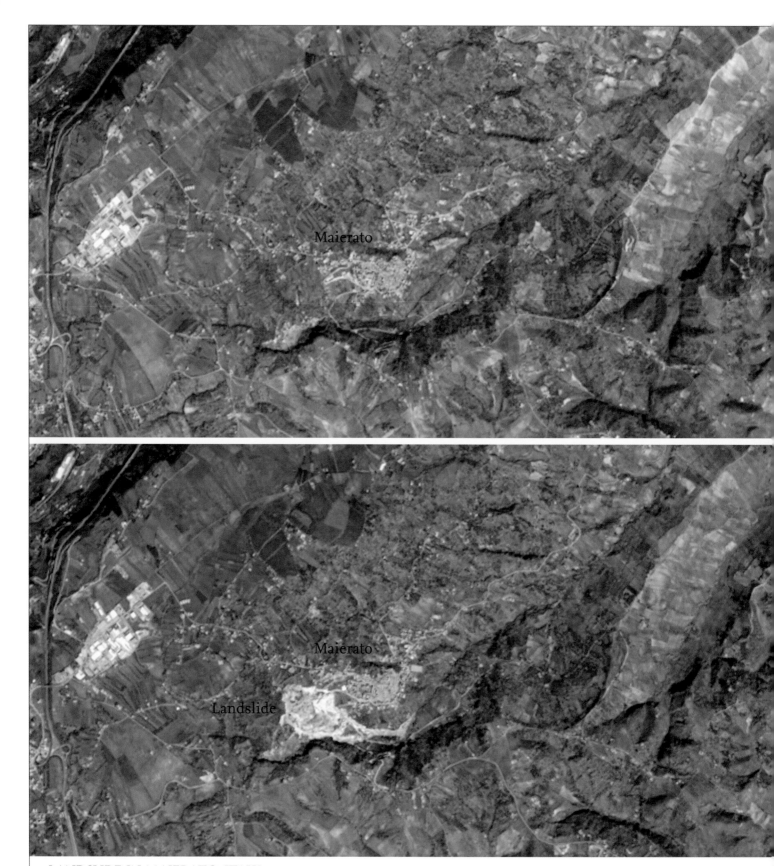

LANDSLIDE IN MAIERATO, ITALY 13 MARCH 2003 AND 14 MARCH 2010

The land around Maierato in Calabria, southern Italy, is steep with a good cover of vegetation. On 15 February 2010 there was heavy rain in the area and it is thought that this contributed to the landslide which happened just outside the town. The town can be seen in the centre of the image. About 200 residents had to be evacuated.

LANDSLIDE IN MAIERATO, ITALY 16 FEBRUARY 2010

The slope which failed had been under stress for some time so the closest residents had been safely evacuated before the slip. There were around 100 other small landslides in the general area at the same time although these do not seem to have affected populated areas except in San Fratello in Sicily.

TROPICAL STORMS

severe and highly destructive storms created by intense low pressure weather systems,
or cyclones, in tropical oceans

Caribbean Storm

NEW ORLEANS, LOUISIANA, USA   28 AUGUST 2002 AND 5 OCTOBER 2005

On a fateful day in October 2005 the unthinkable happened to New Orleans. Category 3 hurricane Katrina, having abated from category 5, struck the Louisiana coast making landfall at probaby the most vulnerable point – New Orleans. The combination of high winds and torrential rain resulted in the levees being breached in a number of places, causing widespread flooding. The satellite images above show the inundation alongside the Inner Harbor Navigation Canal.

GULFPORT, MISSISSIPPI, USA 24 NOVEMBER 2002 AND 2 SEPTEMBER 2005

The effects of the storm surge which can accompany a tropical storm as it makes landfall can be seen in this pair of images of Gulfport, Mississippi, USA. Most noticeable are the three-storey barge which has been left high and dry in the container terminal, and the containers washed inland by the surge, estimated to have been 8–9 m (28–30 feet), a record for an Atlantic storm. It was thought that the damage to the port alone would be in excess of half a billion dollars.

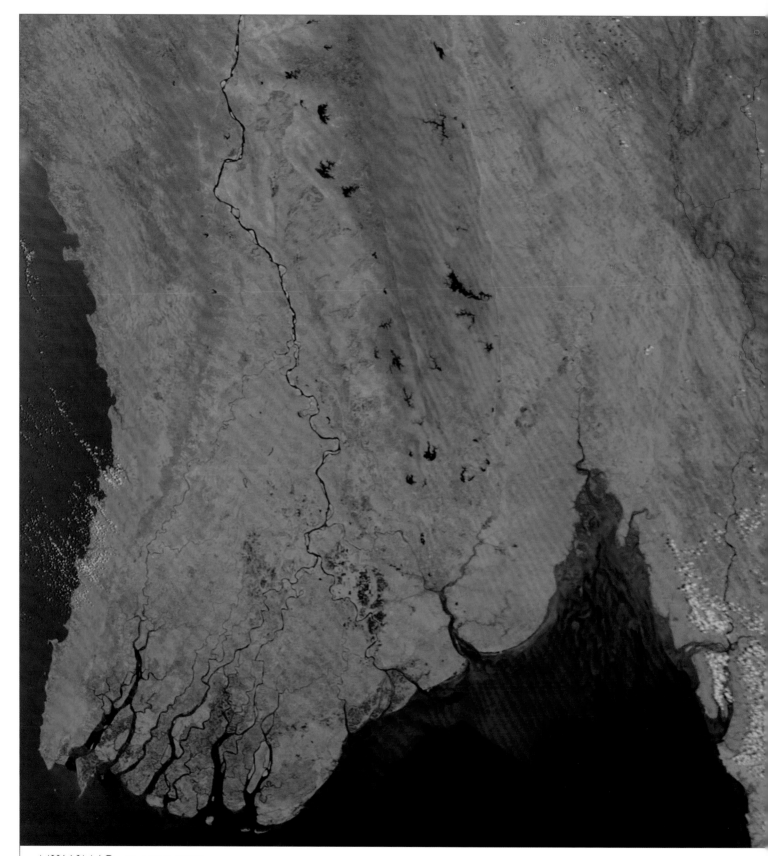

MYANMAR 15 APRIL 2008

In this satellite image lakes and rivers can be clearly seen against the background of vegetation and agricultural land. The main river, the Irrawaddy, flows south and splits into many separate channels becoming a delta known as the Mouths of the Irrawaddy. The darker blue green colour of the coastal wetlands is also clear.

MYANMAR AFTER CYCLONE NARGIS 5 MAY 2008

Cyclone Nargis hit Myanmar on 2 May 2008 with winds of 209 km per hour (130 mph) and gusts of 241–257 km per hour (150–160 mph) which is between a Category 3 and 4 hurricane. There was widespread flooding in the country's most populated area and it is estimated that more than 138 000 people died. The extent of the flood water is quite clear in the later image with many areas, including Yangón, badly affected.

TORNADOES

violent storms with very strong winds circling around small areas of extremely low
pressure, characterized by tall, funnel-shaped clouds

Tornado in Parker, Colorado, USA

NEAR KORCULA, DALMATIAN COAST, CROATIA JULY 2004

This dramatic series of images shows the formation of a waterspout in the Adriatic Sea off the coast of Croatia. The wind speed on the edge of this waterspout reached 170 km (66 miles) per hour but it caused little damage, however, as it did not reach land.

In the first image the air within the cloud has started to rotate and is emerging from it as a funnel. Gradually this funnel extends downwards until it reaches the surface of the sea and the waterspout is formed.

If this had taken place over land it would have become a tornado with a likelihood of damage occurring. In the last two images a second funnel is beginning to form.

It is common for one weather system to spawn a number of tornadoes, resulting in damage over a considerable area as the system tracks across country.

DUSTSTORMS

...torms carrying fine particles into the atmosphere, common in areas of severe drought, ...ausing poor visibility and loss of farmland

Sandstorm, Gaza, Egypt

TIANANMEN SQUARE, BEIJING, CHINA

Tiananmen Square in Beijing is a large open space in the centre of the city. The gate in the picture is the Tiananmen or 'Gate of the Heavenly Peace' which is at the north end of the square.

It was first built in the Ming dynasty in 1420 and is the entrance to the Imperial City. The gate has been rebuilt and renovated several times after fire, war and heavy use toook their toll.

DUST IN TIANANMEN SQUARE, BEIJING, CHINA 2003

When the Spring winds blow from the Gobi Desert they often carry large amounts of sand and dust eastward towards Beijing and onwards to the Korean peninsula and even as far as Japan. In Beijing the sky turns yellow with the dust in the atmosphere, visibility is greatly reduced and the inhabitants have to wear masks to aid with breathing.

GARDEN CITY, KANSAS, USA 1935

Dust storms are by no means a new phenomenon. In the 1930s the Great Plains region of North America was notorious for its frequent dust storms and became known as the 'Dust Bowl'. As a result of poor farming techniques and drought the soil turned to dust and was carried away eastward by the wind, reaching as far as the Atlantic Ocean.

In 1935 these two photographs were taken in Kansas, one of the many states to suffer during the Dust Bowl era. Taken only fifteen minutes apart, it is only the street lights which confirm that the images are of the same scene. After the government promoted soil conservation programmes the area slowly began to rehabilitate.

SNOW

precipitation in the form of flakes of ice crystals formed in the upper atmosphere

Avalanche in the Khumbu Icefall, Nepal

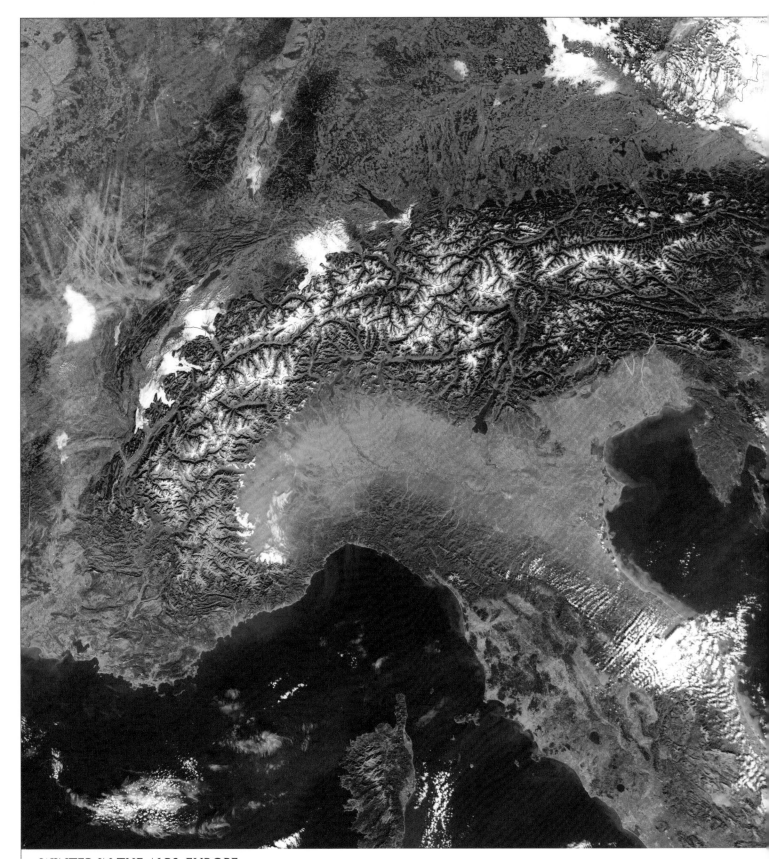

WINTER IN THE ALPS, EUROPE

In November, at the beginning of winter, only the highest peaks and ridges are capped in snow with some having remained snow-covered all year. However, towards the end of the winter the increase in snow cover can be clearly seen on the right-hand satellite image taken in March. Most of the Alpine region is now covered in snow with only the lower valleys being clear.

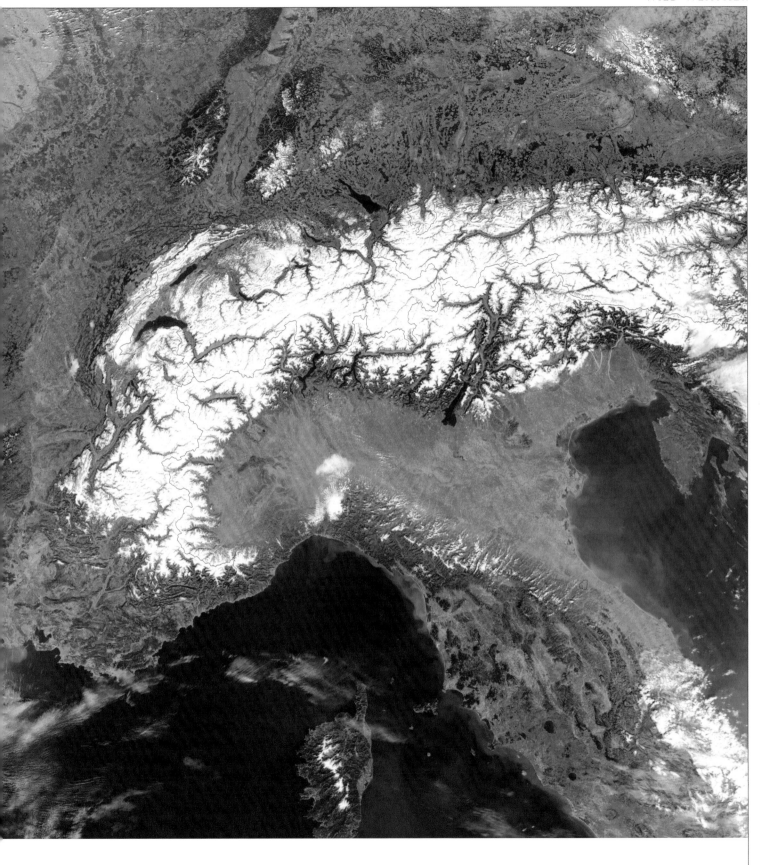

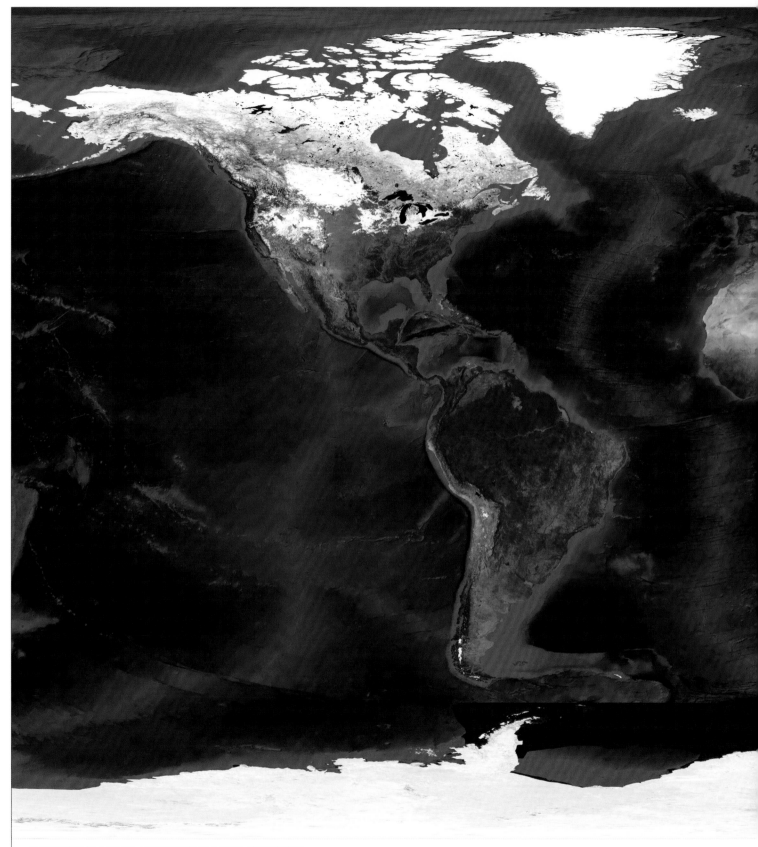

WINTER IN THE NORTHERN HEMISPHERE

Snow cover in January in the northern hemisphere extends in an almost horizontal band as far south as the USA/Canada border and from eastern Europe to northern China. South of this line the high mountain ranges of the Rocky Mountains, the Caucasus, the Himalaya and Japan are snowclad. Western Europe, as a consequence of

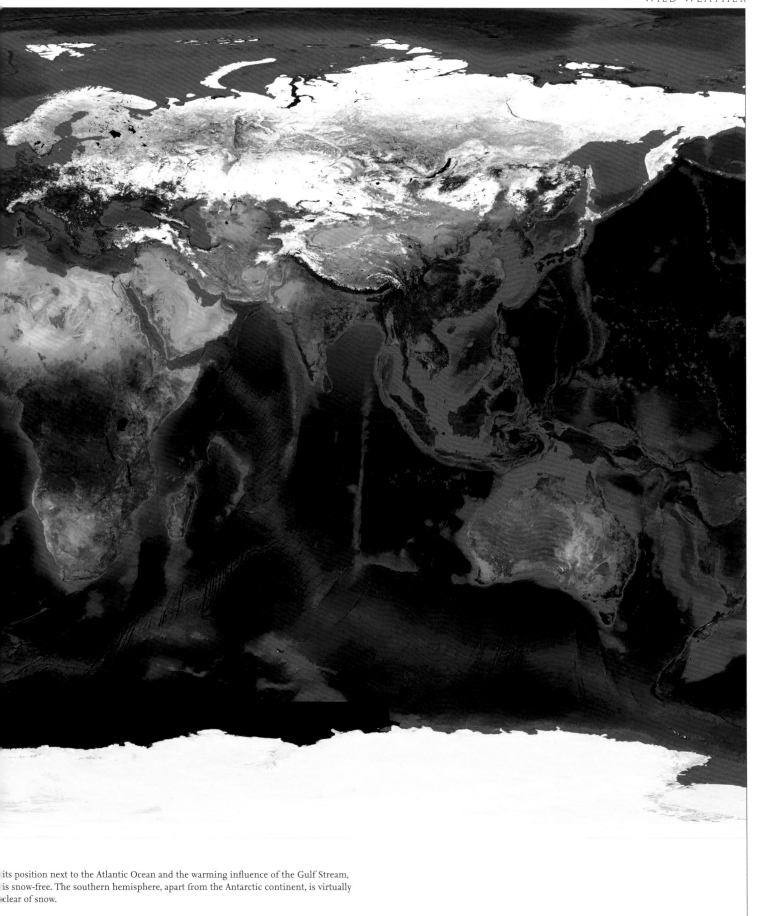

its position next to the Atlantic Ocean and the warming influence of the Gulf Stream, is snow-free. The southern hemisphere, apart from the Antarctic continent, is virtually clear of snow.

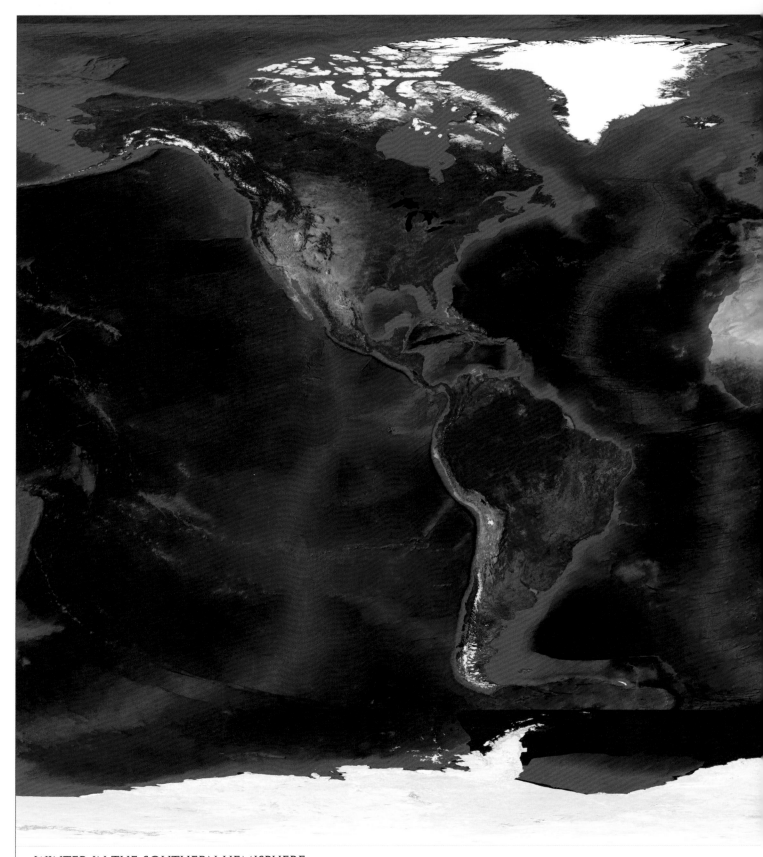

WINTER IN THE SOUTHERN HEMISPHERE

In July the difference in snow cover in the northern hemisphere is immediately obvious with snow now confined to the Arctic regions and the highest mountain ranges. Even though it is now winter in the southern hemisphere there is little evidence of snow except in the Andes in South America and the Southern Alps of New

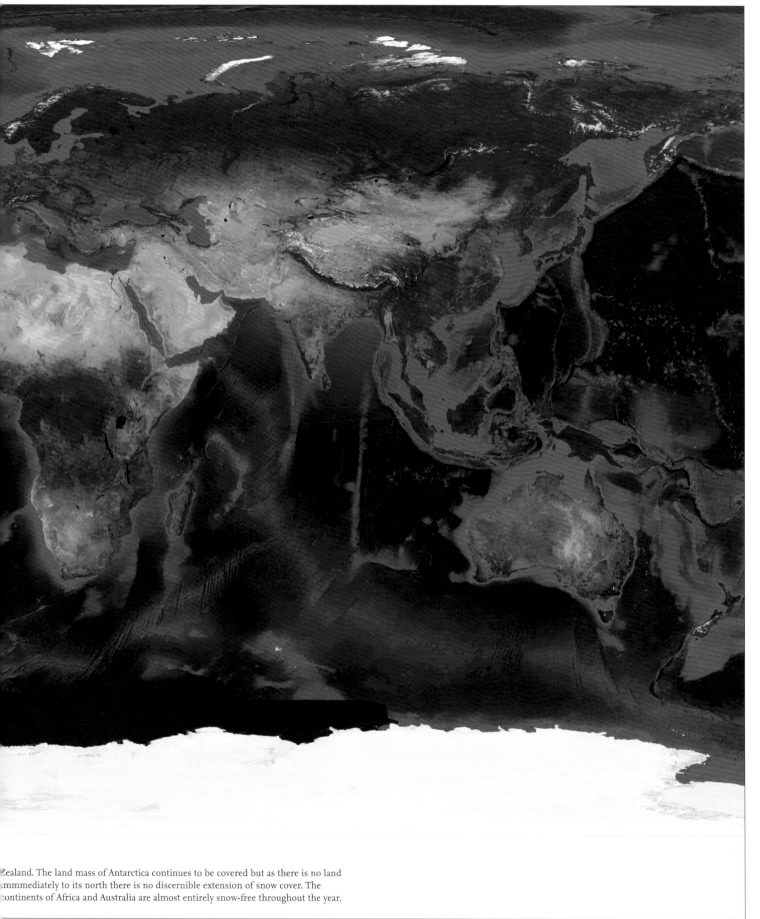

Zealand. The land mass of Antarctica continues to be covered but as there is no land immediately to its north there is no discernible extension of snow cover. The continents of Africa and Australia are almost entirely snow-free throughout the year.

POLAR ICE

permanent and seasonal ice sheets, ice caps and sea ice in the polar regions
of the Arctic and Antarctica

Blue Iceberg

LARSEN ICE SHELF STARTS TO COLLAPSE, ANTARCTICA 17 AND 23 FEBRUARY 2002...

An ice shelf typically advances for several decades until it becomes unstable and icebergs break off, or calve, from the front of the shelf. This advance and retreat is normal and maintains the ice volume. Scientists had predicted that a retreat was due to happen to the Larsen B ice shelf. In the Antarctic summer of 2002, rather than

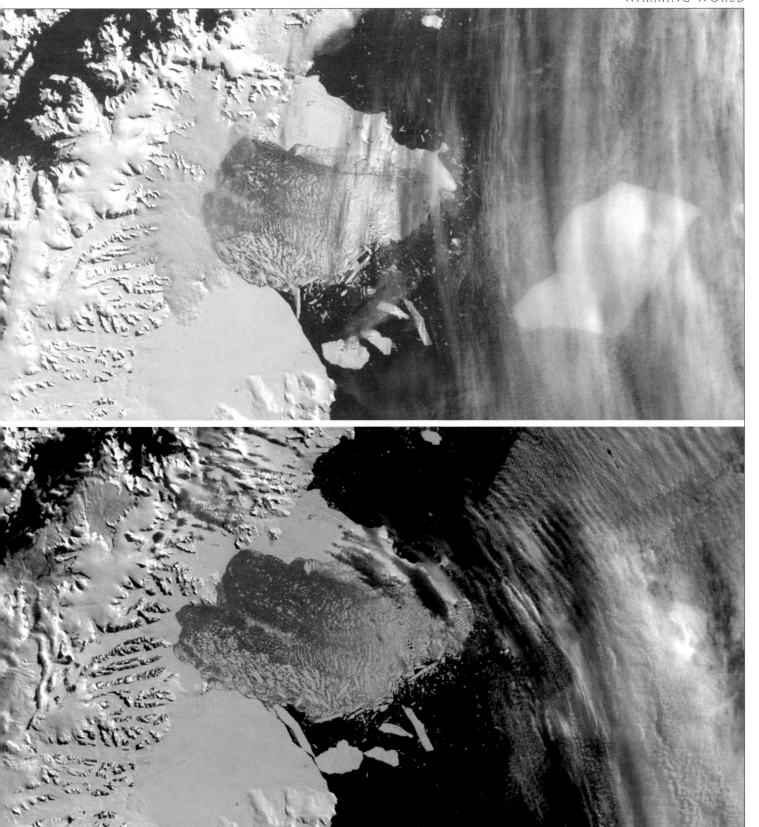

..AND THEN DISINTEGRATES 5 AND 7 MARCH 2002

calving, it completely disintegrated over a 35-day period. It released nearly 3000 sq km (1158 sq miles) of ice, equivalent to an area larger than Luxembourg. This is the largest ice shelf retreat in the Antarctic Peninsula in the last 30 years and is attributed to significant warming of the local climate since the late 1940s.

RONNE-FILCHNER ICE SHELF, ANTARCTICA 12 JANUARY 2010

This ice shelf bordering the Weddell Sea, covers an area of around 430 000 sq km (166 000 sq miles) and is the second largest in Antarctica after the Ross Ice Shelf. The shelf is divided into the Western (Ronne) and Eastern (Filchner) sections which grow due to the flow of the inland ice sheets. When the stress on the ice gets too great, cracks form and parts of the ice sheetbreak away from the ice shelf creating icebergs. This process is known as calving.

RONNE-FILCHNER ICE SHELF, ANTARCTICA 13 JANUARY 2010

n the day between these two images an area around 4000 sq km (1544 sq miles) broke way from the ice shelf and disintegrated into smaller pieces. The narrow tongue of ice here the break-up happened is a bridge of thin sea ice which is anchored to the shore.

This ice bridge regularly breaks up and reforms and is a dramatic introduction to the arrival of summer in Antarctica.

GREENLAND ICE SHEET MELT ZONE 14 JUNE 2001

The ice sheet covering Greenland has an area of 1 833 900 sq km (708 069 sq miles) and an average thickness of 2.3 km (1.4 miles). It is the second-largest concentration of frozen freshwater on Earth and if it were to melt completely the global sea level would rise by up to 7 m (23 feet).

EXPANDING INLAND 14 JUNE 2005

The rapidly expanding melt zone (highlighted) on the western edge of the ice sheet can be seen where the water has darkened the ice to blue-grey. June is in the melting season which reaches its peak in late August or early September. Fortunately, the ice in the interior of the island is still accumulating.

FROZEN IN WINTER ICE, SHISHMAREF, ALASKA, USA 2003

This is a winter view of Shishmaref, a village on Sarichef Island in the Chukchi Sea, just north of the Bering Strait and five miles from mainland Alaska. At this time of the year the sea ice gives protection to the shoreline. In the past it also protected the shore from storm surges for much of the year but now in the summer there is much less ice and the coastline is suffering as a result.

EFFECTS OF MELTING PERMAFROST, SHISHMAREF, ALASKA, USA SEPTEMBER AND OCTOBER 2005

The permafrost which the village is built on is also melting. This makes the shore much more vulnerable to erosion. Recent erosion rates average around 3.3 m (10 feet) per year and buildings are being lost. The community is now faced with moving the village's location or building sea walls to give themselves some of the protection once afforded by the sea ice.

SHRINKING GLACIERS

masses of ice flowing slowly down valleys, whose extent and rate
of movement is affected by climate change

Cerro Torre, Patagonia, Argentina

QORI KALIS GLACIER, PERU 1978

Qori Kalis glacier is the largest outlet from the Quelccaya Ice Cap in southeast Peru. The ice cap has shrunk by approximately 20 per cent since 1963 as the snowline has retreated due to increasing temperatures. Local water supplies and lakes are drying up because of the rising temperatures and lower levels of precipitation.

2002

However, in meltwater season there are floods and landslides. The glacier itself is retreating at an alarming rate.

Between 1998 and 2001 its retreat averaged 155 m (509 feet) per year, 32 times faster than between 1963 and 1978.

MUIR GLACIER, ALASKA   8 AUGUST 1941

Alaska's Glacier Bay has been a National Monument since 1925 and a National Park since 1980. One of the glaciers to be found there is the Muir Glacier which is named after John Muir, the naturalist and explorer who first viewed it on his 1879 expedition.

The southern Alaskan glaciers are sensitive to climate change and many have shrunk or disappeared over the last 100 years.

31 SEPTEMBER 2004

MUIR GLACIER, ALASKA 15 SEPTEMBER 1976

The Muir Glacier is now only a shadow of its former glory, and has nearly retreated up out of the ocean. Many of the large tidewater glaciers that John Muir first saw in 1879 have become small glaciers terminating on land. As the glaciers recede, plants and animals are recolonizing the area. The retreat seems to be caused by higher temperatures and changes in precipitation.

GANGOTRI GLACIER, INDIA 2001

This false-colour satellite image shows the Gangotri Glacier in northern India. At its current length of 30.2 km (18.7 miles) it is one of the longest in the Himalaya. The glacier is the source of the Bhagirathi river, an important tributary of the Ganges river.

It is also a place of traditional Hindu pilgrimage. The Gangotri Glacier has been receding since 1780, and the retreat quickened after 1971. Over the last 25 years the glacier has retreated more than 850 m (2789 feet), with a recession of 76 m (249 feet)

rom 1996 to 1999 alone. This is a concern as the glacial channel which feeds the river as changed course and the volume of water is shrinking rapidly, mainly due to reduced winter precipitation. Local deforestation around the glacier is also adding to the problem and it is feared that parts of the glacier may disintegrate.

GRINNELL GLACIER, MONTANA, USA 1938 AND 2009

The Grinnell Glacier is one of the most photographed glaciers in the Glacier National Park. It is named after the early explorer George Grinnell. These photographs show that while the Grinnell Glacier has retreated significantly from the foreground over the intervening seventy years, the small Gem Glacier above it on a shelf in the mountain has hardly changed. It has been predicted that all the glaciers in the park will have melted by 2030.

BLACKFOOT AND JACKSON GLACIERS, MONTANA, USA 1914 AND 2009

Also in Glacier National Park is the Blackfoot Glacier which was originally measured in 1850 at an area of 7.59 sq km (2.93 sq miles). With its reatreat it has separated into two parts as can be seen on the lower image, the Blackfoot Glacier on the left and and the Jackson Glacier on the right. Together they now cover 2.76 sq km (1.07 sq miles). These glaciers are part of the ongoing United States Geological Survey's Glacier Monitoring Research program, which is researching changes to glaciers in and around Glacier National Park.

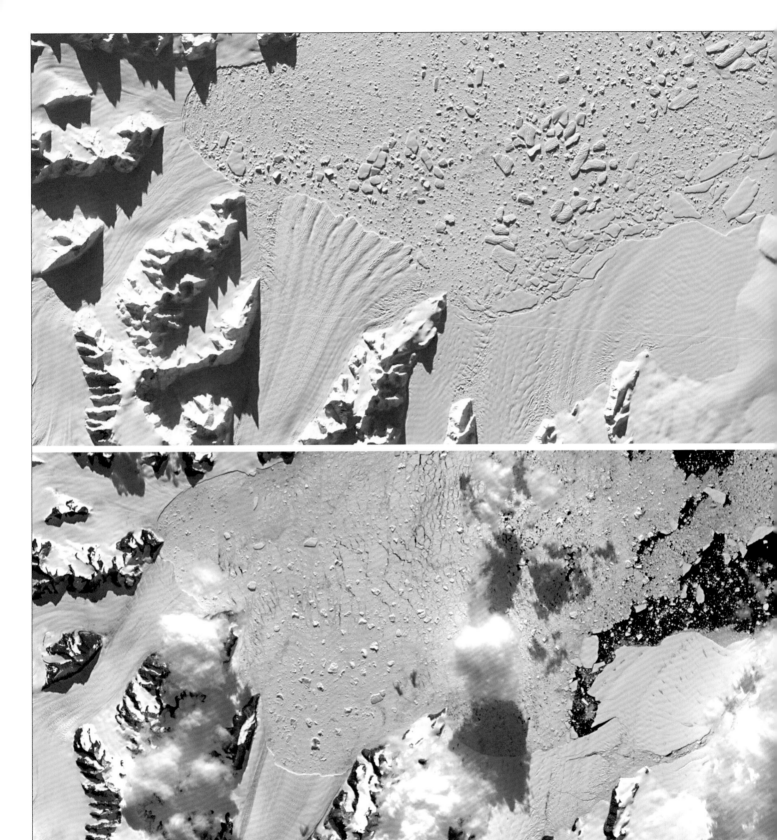

CRANE GLACIER, ANTARCTIC PENINSULA APRIL 2002, FEBRUARY 2003

In 2002 the Larsen B Ice Shelf disintegrated after several very warm summers. The following summer more segments broke away and without the stabilizing influence of the ice shelf the Crane Glacier retreated dramatically. The fan shape of the terminus in the earlier picture becomes C-shaped as the centre of the glacier disintegrated much faster than the edges which were supported by the surrounding mountains.

UPSALA GLACIER, ARGENTINA 1928 AND 2004

The Upsala Glacier is one of the largest Patagonian glaciers. It is a 'calving' glacier which means that when the front of the glacier is in contact with water it loses a significant part of its mass due to large pieces of ice falling off. All parts of this glacier retreated after 1978. However, not all Patagonian glaciers have retreated and the Moreno Glacier, also in Argentina, has even advanced.

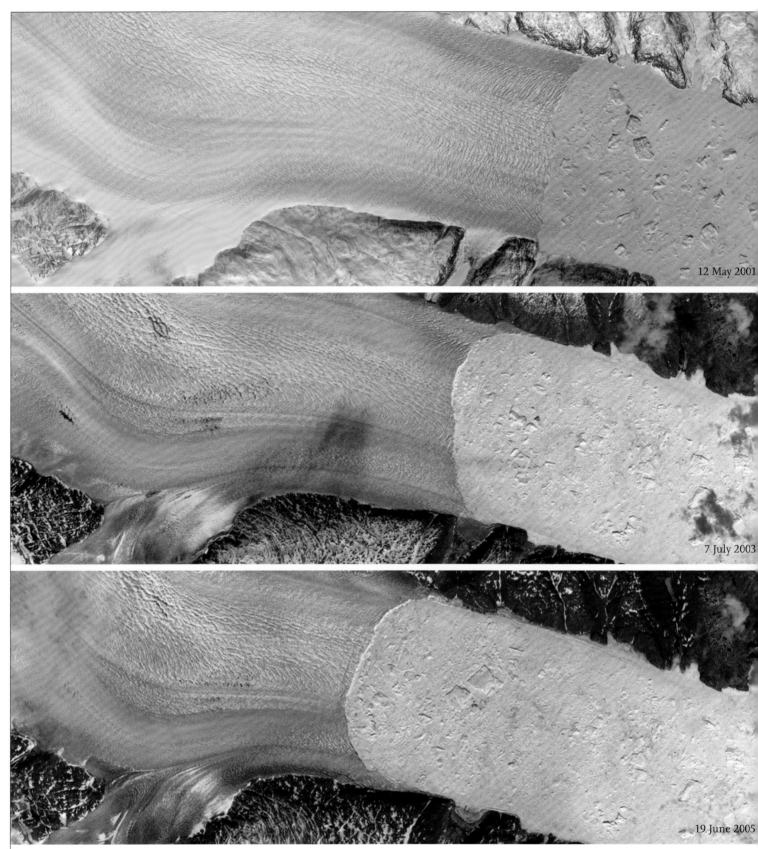

12 May 2001

7 July 2003

19 June 2005

HELHEIM GLACIER RETREAT, GREENLAND 12 MAY 2001, 7 JULY 2003, 19 JUNE 2005

The Helheim Glacier flows into the sea in a narrow fjord and is a calving glacier. From the 1970s up until 2001 the glacier terminus showed little change. However between 2001 and 2005 it retreated by around 7.5 km (4.7 miles). The glacier's rate of flow seems to have speeded up as a result of this and it is now also around 40 m (131 feet) thinner.

BRIKSDALSBREEN GLACIER RETREAT, NORWAY 2004 AND 2009

Briksdalsbreen is a northern arm of the Jostedalsbreen Glacier and it terminates in a small lake. It is a glacier which is affected by temperature and precipitation. It advanced in the early twentieth century then retreated mid-century exposing the lake. It was unusual in the 1990s as it advanced when other European glaciers were retreating. Since 2000 it has been retreating again and the terminus is now on land. It is thought this is its smallest extent since the 1200s.

ALETSCH GLACIER, SWITZERLAND

The Aletsch Glacier is the largest Alpine glacier in central Europe. It covers a distance of around 23 km (14 miles) with an area of around 120 sq km (45 sq miles). The glacier is central in the satellite image. The Fiescher and Aar glaciers are to the east. Most of the highest summits of the Bernese Alps are located in this area, the Jungfrau and Mönch to the north, the Gross Fiescherhorn and Gross Wannenhorn to the east, and the Aletschhorn to the west.

ALETSCH GLACIER, SWITZERLAND

The area of the Aletsch Glacier and some of the surrounding valleys is on the UNESCO World Heritage list. It is a popular destination for tourists with glacier tours available while cable cars and the Jungfraujoch railway help with access. This image shows the glacier terminus. The dark stripe of the moraine, which is a feature of this glacier, is just visible. The glacier has reatreated around 3 km (1.8 miles) since 1860. It is currently retreating at a rate of about 50 m (164 feet) a year.

RISING SEA LEVELS

verage height of the level of the surface of the world's oceans and seas,
kely to rise as a result of global warming

Camogli, Italy

LOW TIDE IN TUVALU

Tuvalu is an island nation in the Pacific Ocean. Its inhabitants live mainly on coral atolls which are very low-lying. Many of its islands are only a few metres above sea level at their highest point. Over recent years the islanders have seen many changes in their fortunes, but the most important issue now to most is that as the tide comes in, their property is at risk of flooding.

HIGH TIDES ARE GETTING HIGHER

Warming of the oceans has raised sea levels in parts of the Pacific and certain low-lying island groups, such as Tuvalu, are now very vulnerable. They face the prospect of losing their national identity as more and more inhabitants relocate to countries such as New Zealand.

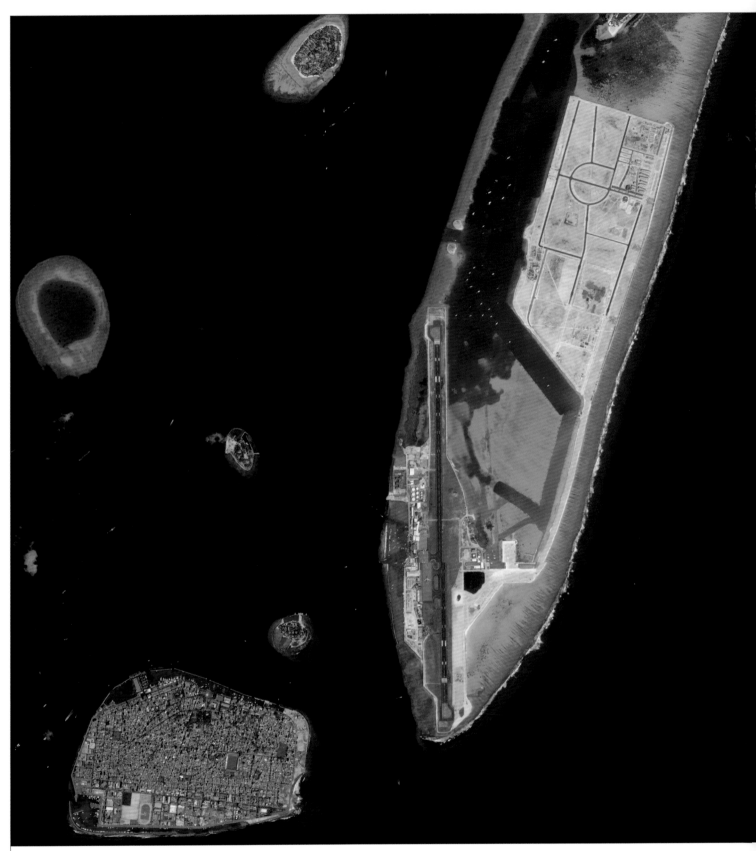

THE MALDIVES, INDIAN OCEAN...

In the Maldives, in the Indian Ocean, storms do not raise the water level by more than around 300 mm (11.8 inches). Accordingly, development has been concentrated on land only 40 cm (15.7 inches) or more above sea level. This means that they are very vulnerable to sea level rise. Most of the population lives within 2 m (6.5 feet) of sea level and almost all within 4 m (13.1 feet).

..LOW-LYING AND VULNERABLE TO SEA LEVEL RISE

Male, the capital of the Maldives, is approximately 2 m (6.5 feet) above the sea, but its reclaimed land is lower. After storms in 1987 and 1988 flooded the reclaimed areas, a series of breakwaters on the outer coast were built to protect the town from damaging storm waves, but they will not prevent flooding from a sustained rise in sea level.

HATTERAS AIRFIELD, NORTH CAROLINA, USA 17 JULY 1996 AND 8 AUGUST 1999

The east coast of the USA is affected by rising sea levels, damage from hurricanes, and other storms, all of which combine to change the coastline and to make parts of it very vulnerable to the sea at high tide. The lower post-hurricane image shows how quickly this can happen in an area where barrier islands are actively moving westwards toward the mainland.

HATTERAS LIGHTHOUSE, NORTH CAROLINA, USA 17 JULY 1996 AND 8 AUGUST 1999

The famous Cape Hatteras lighthouse is the tallest brick lighthouse in the USA at 63 m (208 feet). It was built 488m (1600 feet) from the sea in 1870. Because the barrier islands are moving westwards it could not be protected from the sea indefinitely so in 1999 it was moved a similar distance inland.

VENICE, ITALY

The city of Venice covers 117 islands in the saltwater Venetian Lagoon. The buildings are constructed on closely spaced wooden piles with the foundations of the brick or stone buildings on top. Today the city is one of the top tourist destinations in the world. Among its main sights is St Mark's Basilica, one of the best known examples of Byzantine architecture, built in 832 and now the cathedral church of the Roman Catholic Archdiocese of Venice.

HIGH WATER IN VENICE, ITALY

In winter Venice experiences a few exceptional tides, the 'acqua alta'. This is due to a combination of factors such as astronomical tide, strong south winds, some subsidence of the city over time and the Adriatic 'seiche' wave movement.

Lower-lying parts of the city such as St Mark's Square are most often affected, but only for a few hours until the tide ebbs. Visitors make use of the 'passarele' walkway to visit the basilica when this happens.

DEFORESTATION

he felling of trees, often illegally and in an unmanaged way, commonly to provide land
or agriculture or industry

Wildfire in South Africa

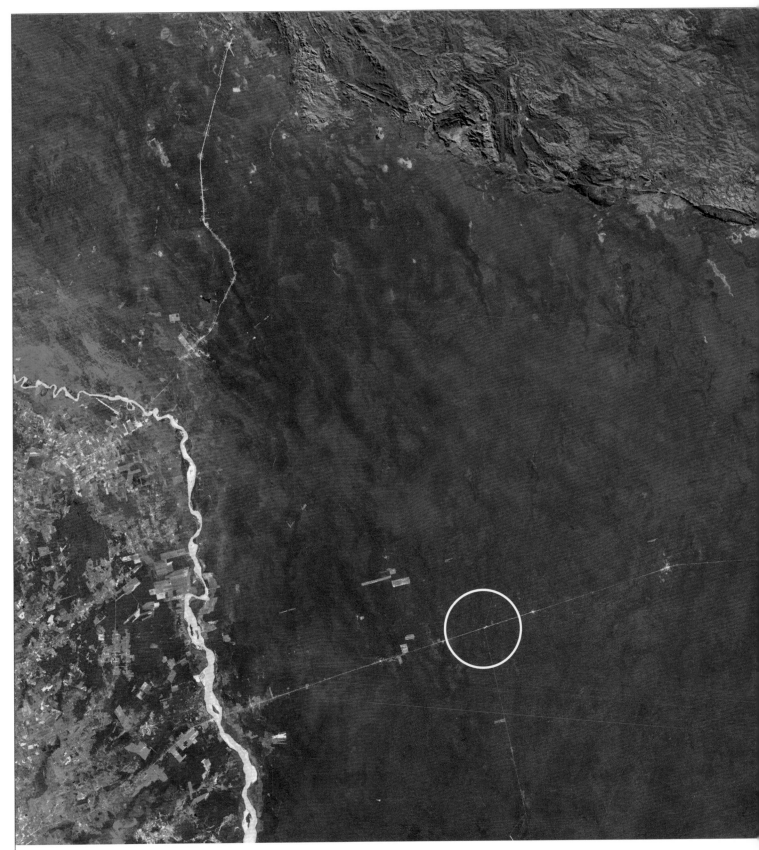

TROPICAL RAINFOREST, SANTA CRUZ, BOLIVIA JUNE 1975

In 1975, the area adjacent to the Rio Grande ó Guapay river, northeast of the Bolivian city of Santa Cruz, was one of rich, dense rainforest crossed by a handful of tracks. The whole region was sparsely populated with only occasional forest clearings visible in this satellite image. Increased agricultural activity is evident in the lower left corner, towards the city.

LOST FOREST, NEW FARMLAND MAY 2003

By 2003, after a period of extensive deforestation, the area had been transformed into a major agricultural area, mainly growing soya beans for export. The population of Santa Cruz has increased from less than 30 000 to over 1 million in the last 35 years. This has put enormous pressure on the forest with an increasing demand for new settlements and farmland.

IGUAÇU FALLS, ARGENTINA, BRAZIL AND PARAGUAY FEBRUARY 1973

Some of the most spectacular waterfalls in the world, the Iguaçu Falls, lie at the junction of Argentina, Brazil and Paraguay. The isolation of this region gave rise to the unique Paranaense rain forest ecosystem which supported thousands of species unique to the region. This satellite image shows early evidence of deforestation with patterns of tree felling following lines of communication.

THIRTY YEARS LATER... MAY 2003

Over a period of thirty years the changes have been dramatic. Vast areas of forest have been cleared for agriculture, particularly in Paraguay on the left of the image. This process was accelerated by the creation of a huge new reservoir, following the construction of the Itaipu Dam (circled) on the Paraná river in the early 1980s. Some forest on the right of the image lies within Iguaçu National Park and has been protected from destruction.

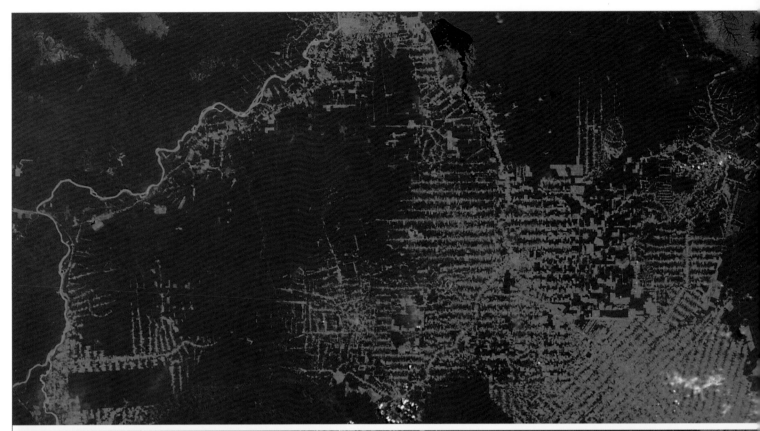

AMAZON DEFORESTATION, RONDÔNIA, BRAZIL 2000 AND 2003

Rondônia is one of the parts of the Amazon most affected by deforestation. The areas cleared of forest show up in the satellite images as tan, while crops and pasture show as light green. In this area the cleared forest moves both northwest and northeast along the roads. By 2003 it was estimated that nearly 68 000 sq km (over 26 000 sq miles) of the forest in the state had been cleared. This represents around one third of all the forest in the state. Over time a pattern emerges in the images. Early clearings

AMAZON DEFORESTATION, RONDÔNIA, BRAZIL 2006 AND 2009

ook like fishbones extending out from the roads. These become a mix of cleared areas, settlements and some uncleared areas. Not all of the roads are legal, but small farmers still migrate to these areas, clear land for crops and when after a short time the rain and erosion affect the soil and the crop yields fall away, they use it for cattle pasture and move to another area to clear. When they have cleared all the land they claimed it often ends up merged with other claims as large areas of cattle pasture.

ADVANCING DESERTS

the encroachment of desert conditions into settlements or agricultural areas
as a result of climate change or bad farming practices

Namib Desert, Namibia

THE EDGE OF THE DESERT, SAHEL REGION, AFRICA

Many parts of the world, on the delicate fringes between fertile and arid regions, are at risk from advancing deserts. This is shown graphically in this image of the Sahel region of Africa. The Sahel is a buffer zone between the Sahara Desert to the north and the savannah grasslands to the south. Sand dunes are also threatening oases in

he desert and various measures are being taken to try to restrict the advance of sand onto valuable arable and cattle-rearing land. Climate change and man's destruction of natural vegetation are exacerbating the problem and threatening the traditional way of life in many areas.

PROTECTING THE TRANS SAHARAN HIGHWAY, MAURITANIA 2003

There are many ways of controlling advancing deserts, such as planting trees and nitrogen-fixing plants, or spraying petroleum over seeded land to prevent moisture loss. Or more simply, as along the Trans Saharan Highway in Mauritania, by erecting fences to slow down the encroachment of the sand dunes.

ON THE DESERT'S EDGE, LANGTOU GOU, HEBEI, CHINA 2000

ne of the areas most threatened by advancing desert is the land which lies to the east f the Gobi Desert in China. The village of Langtou Gou lies only 130 km (81 miles) from the capital Beijing and it is being threatened by sand blowing from the Gobi, destroying fields and covering houses.

DROUGHT AND FIRE

rolonged period of dry weather leading to water shortages, loss of crops and
n increased risk of fire

Dried out Lake Amboseli, Kenya

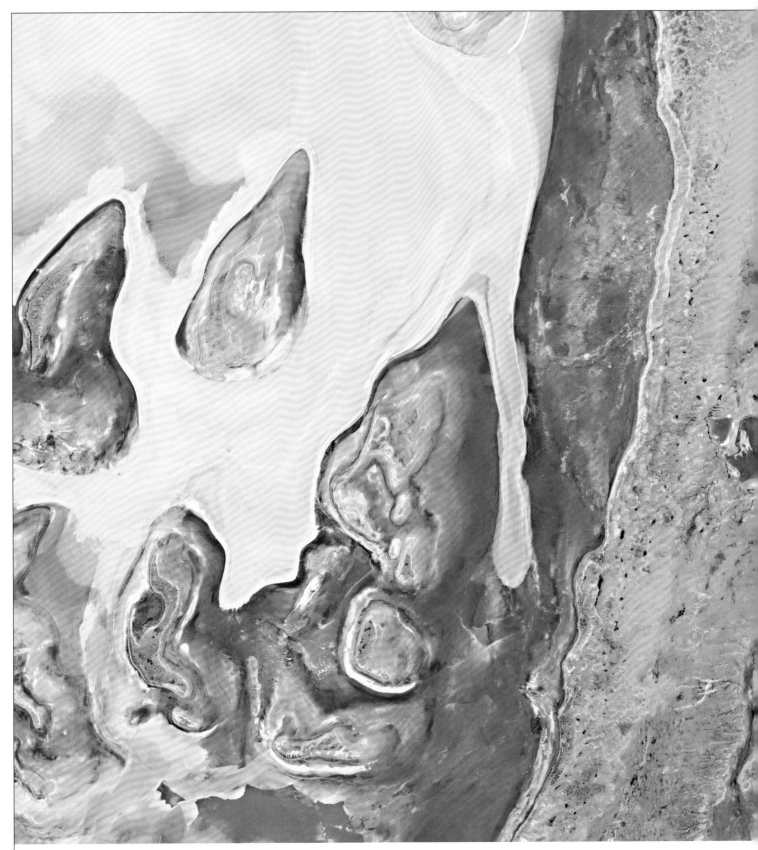

LAKE FROME, AUSTRALIA 2009

Lake Frome is the most southerly of the lakes that make up an endorheic, or closed, drainage basin in the area to the east of the Flinders Ranges. As this area receives very little rain in an average year these lakes are usually saltpans. This satellite image of the eastern edge of the lake shows the normal view of dry river channels, with the uneven surface of the saltpan filled with dry sediment.

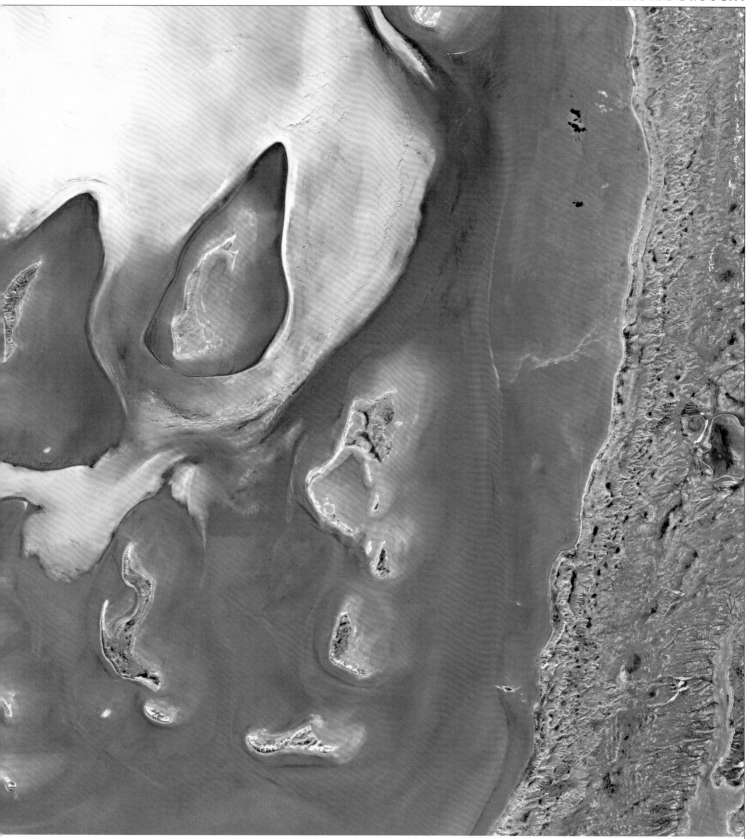

LAKE FROME, AUSTRALIA 2010

Some rains do make it into Lake Frome as overflow from Lake Callabonna to the north or from rain in the northern Flinders Ranges. In early 2010 rains in central Australia caused severe flooding with impermanent rivers being filled all the way from Queensland to South Australia. Gradually the water travelled southwards and eventually some made its way to Lake Frome, which was one of the last areas to fill with water, where it appears green as a muddy 'river'.

EFFECTS OF DROUGHT, AUSTRALIA...

Drought affects both man and animals. The Australian drought resulted in waterholes
drying up, with wild animals forced to seek out any available water.

..AND BURKINA, AFRICA

n Burkina, the lowering of the water table necessitates the deepening of wells. In this
mage the man's partner is 10 m (33 feet) below the surface digging the well.

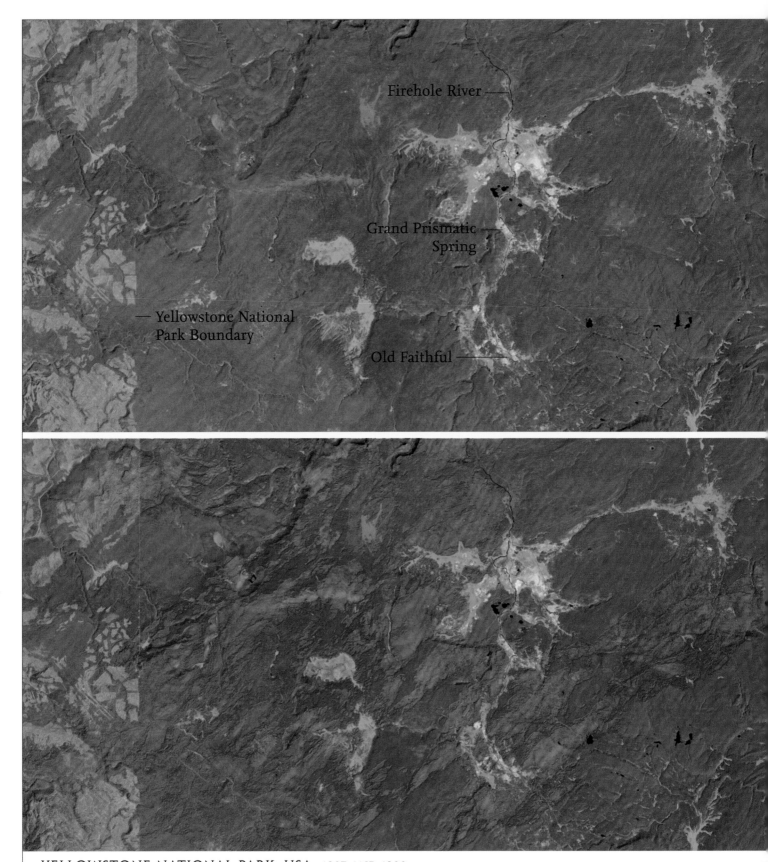

Firehole River ——

Grand Prismatic —— Spring

— Yellowstone National Park Boundary

Old Faithful ————

YELLOWSTONE NATIONAL PARK, USA 1987 AND 1988

During the hot, dry summer of 1988 thunderstorms crossed Yellowstone National Park and the associated lightning set fire to the dry vegetation. By the end of the summer there had been 50 wildfires and approximately 35 per cent of the park had been affected. In the 1987 image there is dense mature pine forest showing dark green, with light green meadow, light blue geyser fields and dark blue lakes. In 1988 the burn scars are dark red, some fires still show pink and there is a haze of smoke.

YELLOWSTONE NATIONAL PARK, USA 1989 AND 2008

In 1989 the full extent of the fire damage can be seen. There are burn scars all around the area of Old Faithfull in the bottom right, but not everything was damaged. The burns are patchy and some areas experienced less damage than others. Fire helps the lodgepole pine and grassy meadows of the park to regenerate, but the environment means that regeneration is slow. Twenty years on from the fire the 2008 image shows the forest is returning and the burn scar is fading as new trees grow.

DRYING LAKES AND RIVERS

reduction in the size of lakes and river flow rates due to climate change
or the extraction of water for agriculture or industry

Dry river bed in the Dead Vlei, Namibia

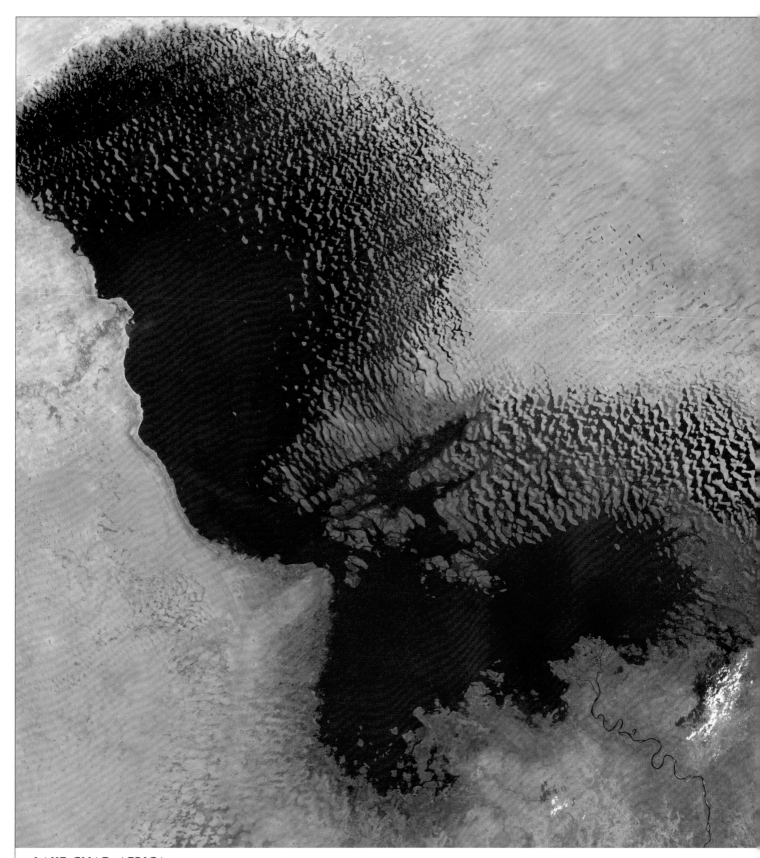

LAKE CHAD, AFRICA 1972

Lake Chad was once one of the largest lakes in Africa, but as a result of extensive irrigation projects, the encroaching desert and an increasingly dry climate, it is now a twentieth of its former size. As the lake floor is flat and shallow, the water level fluctuates seasonally with the rainfall. The fifteen years from 1972 to 1987 saw the most

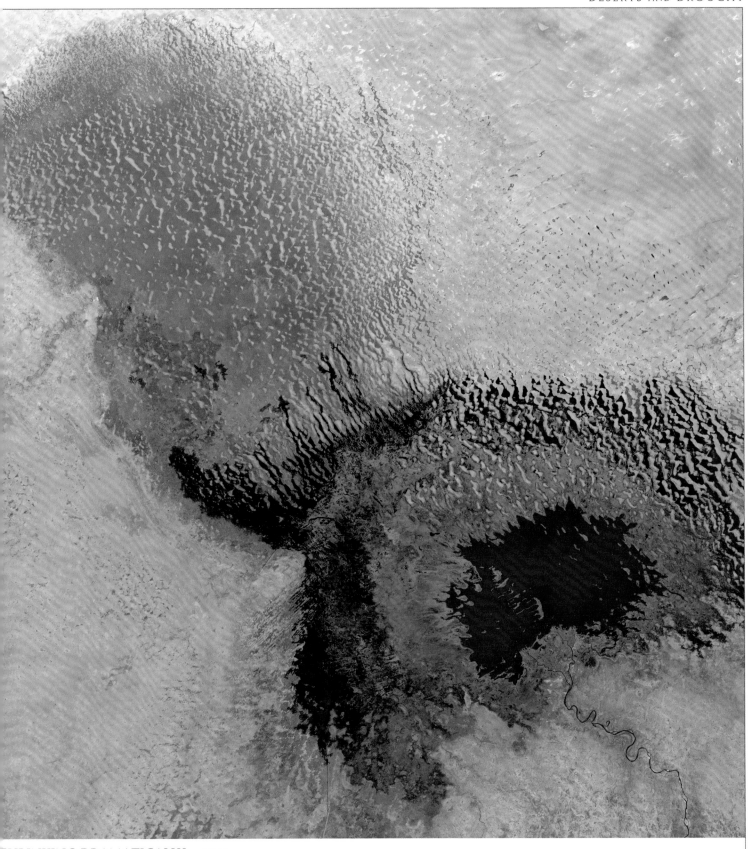

SHRINKING DRAMATICALLY... 1987

dramatic change in the lake, as illustrated in these two satellite images. This dramatic change was the result of an increase in water being diverted for irrigation. Now, with a drying climate, the desert is taking over, as is shown by the ripples of wind-formed sand dunes where the northern half of the lake used to be.

125

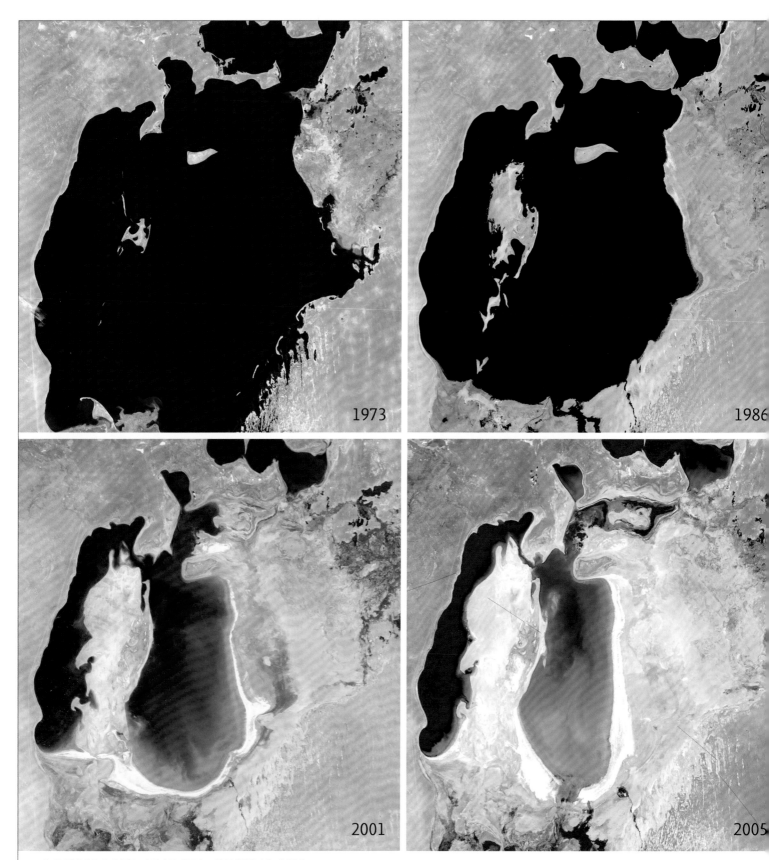

1973

1986

2001

2005

A DYING LAKE, ARAL SEA, CENTRAL ASIA

The Aral Sea was once the world's fourth-largest lake. Today, due to climate change and the diversion of water from its feeder rivers for irrigation, it is much smaller. Steps have been taken to preserve the northern part by constructing a dam, but the southern part has been abandoned to its fate.

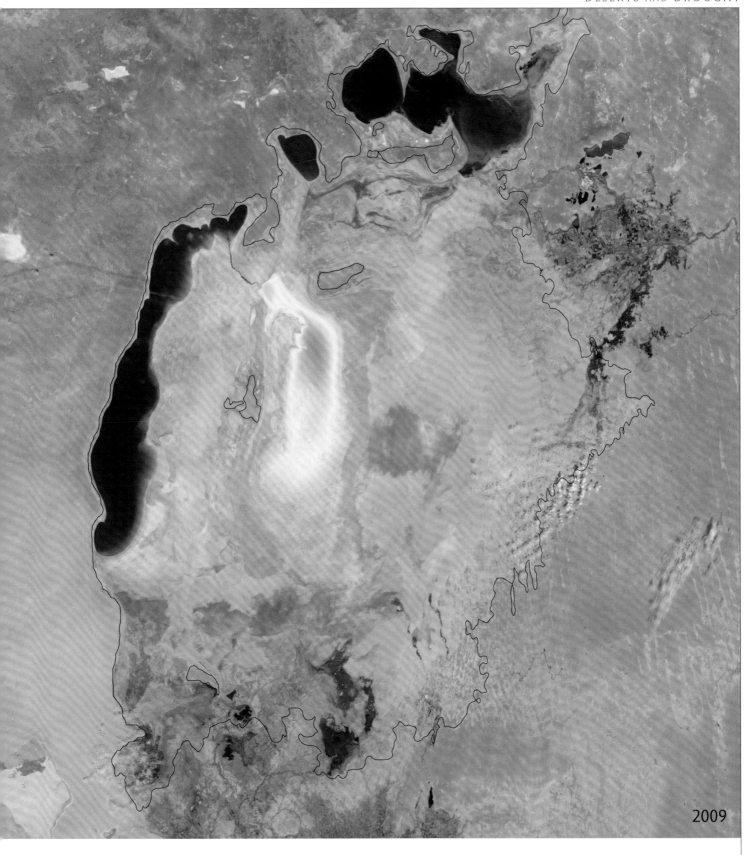

2009

The local fishing industry on the Aral Sea has been devastated by the lake's shrinkage and the local population has developed health problems due to the exposure of chemicals on the dry sea bed. Abandoned ships litter the former lake bed and as it dries out vast salt plains are forming and dust storms are becoming more frequent.

Dirty Devil River

Narrow Canyon
(Colarado River)

Mille Crag Bend

Hite Marina

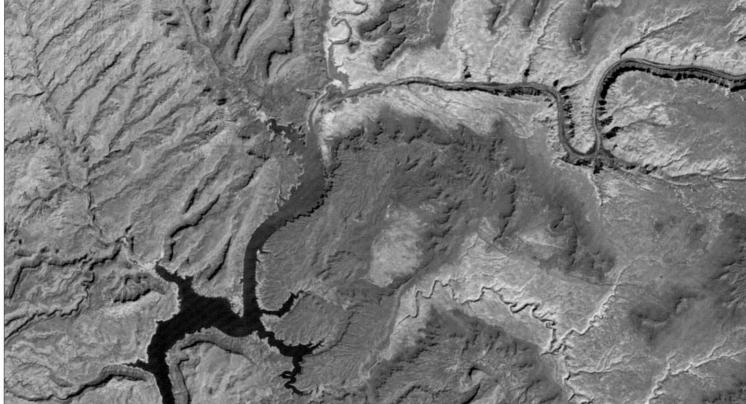

FLUCTUATING WATER LEVELS IN LAKE POWELL, USA 1999 AND 2003

Lake Powell is one of the lakes created along the Colorado river to manage the flood water from the spring snowmelt in the Rocky Mountains and also to provide a reliable water supply. The Glen Canyon Dam created Lake Powell, which is downstream of these images that show the very north of the lake where the Dirty Devil river joins the Colorado. From 1999, when the lake was near full capacity, there was a prolonged drought and by 2003 canyon floor features could be seen in the Narrow Canyon at the top of the image.

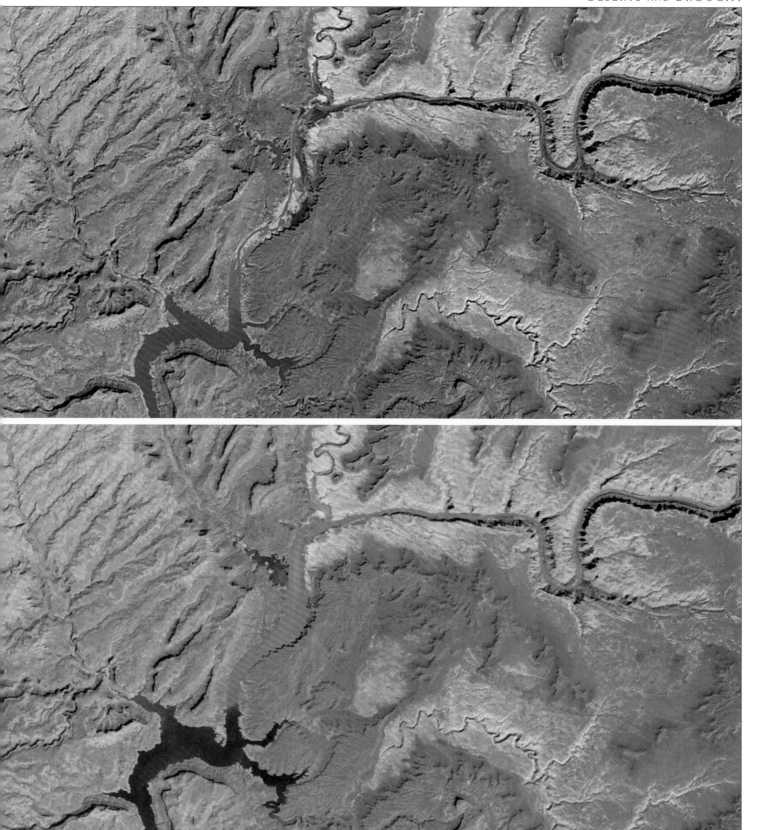

LUCTUATING WATER LEVELS IN LAKE POWELL, USA 2005 AND 2009

y 2005 the lake was at its lowest level with isolated pools of water and large areas of xposed canyon floor. After 2005 the drought conditions improved. Rainfall was not ack to normal but by April 2010, although the level of water in the lake was not as

that of 1999, the flow of water into the lake was around 94.5 per cent of the average. Drought in this area is not uncommon, but with climate changes there are predictions that rainfall may decline by 20–25 per cent in the future.

COLORADO RIVER, USA 2002

These two images of the Colorado River as it enters Lake Powell illustrate the effect of low rainfall in the western USA as seen on the satellite images on the previous pages. The Lake Powell reservoir level had fallen by 13 m (43 feet) in the eighteen months between photos. By 2005 the lake was at its lowest ever level.

COLORADO RIVER, USA 2003

lthough by 2009 the lake level had improved there will be long term challanges
 supply water to an ever expanding urban population, especially if the rainfall
eclines as is predicted.

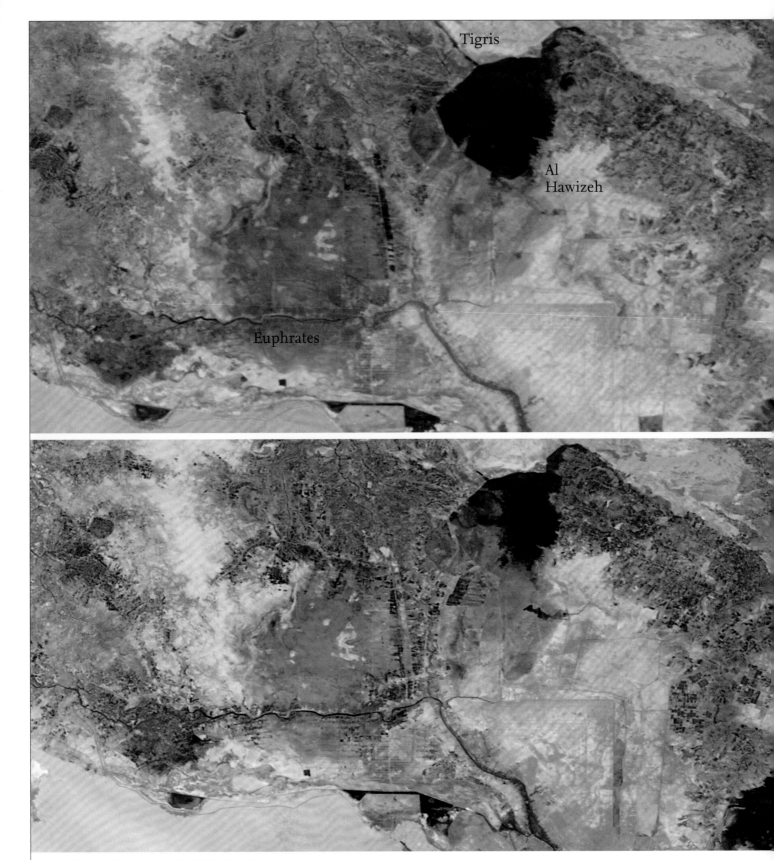

MESOPOTAMIA MARSHES, IRAQ 2000 AND 2003

The wetlands of Mesopotamia were once an area diverse in plant and animal life, a rare aquatic landscape in the desert. Over time the volume of water reaching them has been much reduced by dams to control floods, canals, reservoirs and hydroelectric schemes.

In the 1990s they were drained by former Iraqi leader Saddam Hussein, partly as a punishment to the local tribes who had taken part in anti-government rebellions. In 2000 there is only one large remnant of marsh, Al Hawizeh, and this was to shrink further as spring floods no longer reached it.

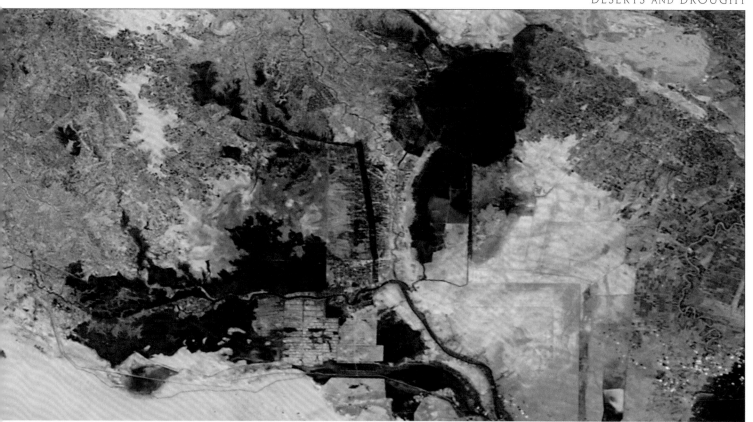

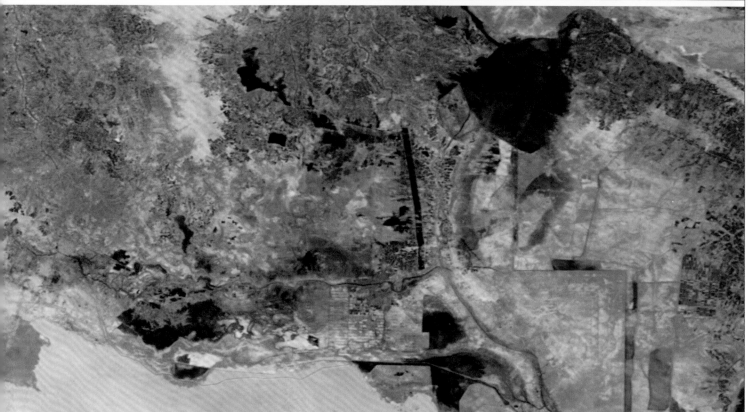

MESOPOTAMIA MARSHES, IRAQ 2007 AND 2010

After the end of the Second Gulf War in 2003, many of the canals draining the marsh were demolished, several large marsh areas flooded again, Al Hawizeh expanded and irrigated crops were grown as can be seen in 2007. A drought in 2009 had a severe impact on the area, affecting crops, but in 2010 while some marshes have shrunk, irrigated crops seem to be extensive and healthy. There are still problems to be faced, the marshes are not connected as they once were and the incoming water levels may fall again as more extensive agriculture picks up elsewhere.

LAKE PALACE HOTEL, UDAIPUR, RAJASTHAN, INDIA *c.1998*

Udaipur, known as the City of Lakes, has many Rajput palaces. The most famous of
these is the Lake Palace, built entirely of marble on a small island in Pichola Lake.
Operating as a luxury hotel, until recently it was accessible only by boat.

STRANDED ON THE LAKE BED   JULY 2005

As a result of severe drought in Rajasthan and seepage of water, the lake recently dried
out. This photograph shows the hotel high and dry and having lost some of its
romantic appeal. Since 2005 the lake has refilled with water.

CHANGING COASTLINES

he action of the sea and rivers in the erosion of coastal features
.nd the deposition of sediment along the coast

Pancake rocks, Punakaiki, New Zealand

LINES OF DEFENCE, BAWDSEY, SUSSEX, UK   25 JANUARY 2005 TO 20 AUGUST 2005

The coast around Bawdsey in Sussex, UK is eroding fast. The *Lines of Defence* flags seen here were part of an art project called *If ever you're in the area*. The complete set of project images beautifully illustrate the problem as they cover a full year.

These three images illustrate the erosion from January to August 2005, by which time approximately 14 m (46 feet) of coastline had been lost.

CULBIN BAR, MORAY FIRTH, SCOTLAND, UK 11 JUNE 1968 AND SEPTEMBER 1993

This 7 km (4 miles) of raised shingle bar is unusual in the UK, where many coastal features of this type have been built on or removed. Culbin Bar is a virtually untouched remnant of a much larger area of sand and shingle coastline. It seems to have started out as a spit growing from the eastern shore of the river Findhorn. The bar changes shape due to erosion at its eastern end and active deposition at its western end. The shingle ridges across it show the effects of this process over time.

HAPPISBURGH, NORFOLK, UNITED KINGDOM AUGUST 2001 AND AUGUST 2005

The 1950s wooden sea defences at Happisburgh have failed and large chunks of cliff regularly fall into the sea. This part of the Norfolk coastline is soft and vulnerable to coastal storms. As seen in this pair of photographs, several buildings have vanished over a period of four years with homes, businesses, roads and the lifeboat station all at risk. In 2010 the village was given a grant to help it adjust to the problems.

WASHINGTON STATE, USA OCTOBER 1997 AND APRIL 1998

The west coast of the USA is vulnerable to storm damage. These photographs were taken as part of a project to record coastal erosion resulting from severe storms generated as part of the Pacific Ocean warming effect of El Niño. In just one winter a significant amount of coastline has vanished leaving more buildings exposed.

THE TWELVE APOSTLES, VICTORIA, AUSTRALIA 9:17 AM 3 JULY 2005

The Twelve Apostles are famous Australian coastal landmarks, which were created by the sea gradually eroding soft limestone cliffs. Cliffs are eroded into headlands, in which caves then form. When caves break through a headland a sea arch is formed, then when an arch collapses a sea stack is left.

ONE MINUTE LATER... 9:18 AM 3 JULY 2005

The Twelve Apostles are now only eight in number. These two images were taken less than one minute apart on a Sunday morning, when one of the 50 m (164 ft) high stacks gave way to the power of the sea and collapsed into a pile of rubble, much to the shock of onlookers.

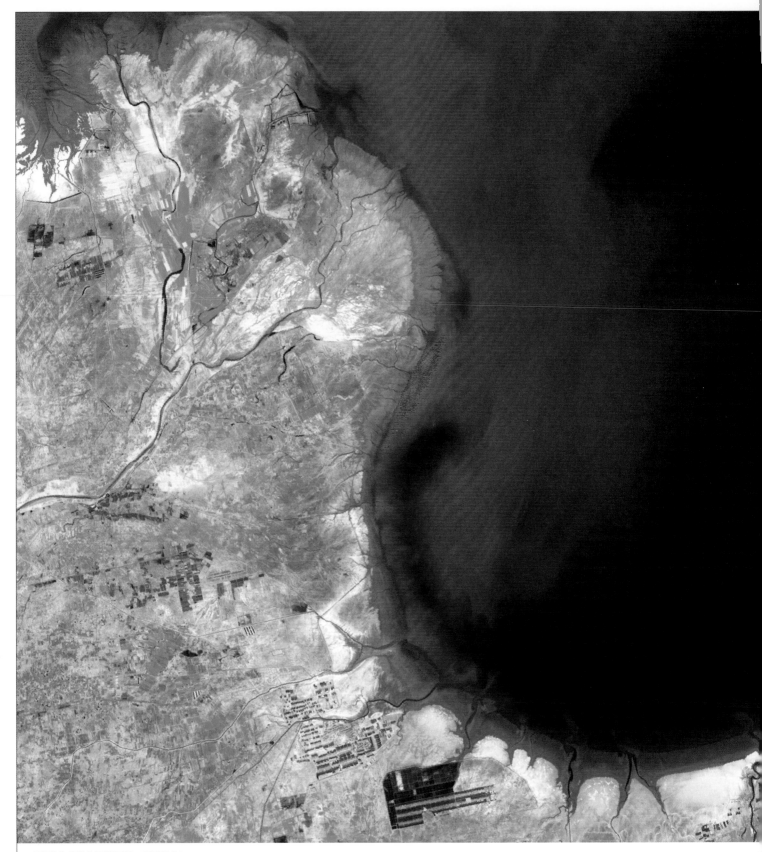

YELLOW RIVER, CHINA 27 MAY 1979

The Yellow River (Huang He) gets its name from the colour of the sediment it carries.
This is mainly mica, quartz and feldspar and as the river travels through north central
China it crosses an easily eroded loess plateau.

Loess is called huang tu, or 'yellow earth' in Chinese, and is a fine-grained deposit
which is very susceptible to wind and water erosion.

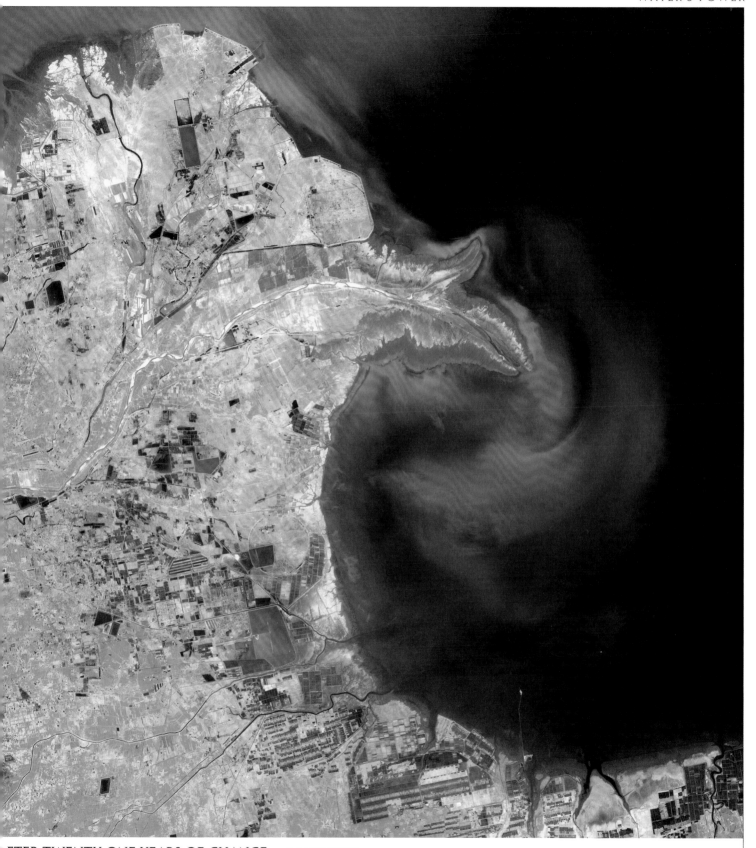

AFTER TWENTY-ONE YEARS OF CHANGE... 2 MAY 2000

nce the river reaches the coast it flows into the sea where the sediments drop out of he current and are deposited into the river delta. In recent years the build-up has been quite dramatic. These images are only twenty-one years apart and in that time a significant amount of new land has been created.

CAPE HATTERAS, NORTH CAROLINA, USA 1999

Cape Hatteras is part of a barrier island system on the coast of North Carolina. As a result of rising sea levels, strong storms and warming of the air and ocean, these islands are migrating westward. Between 1870 and 1919 the coast in this area migrated westward by 365 m (1200 feet) and since then there has been a battle to prevent further erosion, including building breakwaters and importing sand.

FIVE YEARS LATER 2004

By 2004 we can see how much the coastline of this important tourist area has moved in just five years, leaving this and many other houses nearby close to destruction. Insurance money is often used for building large beach houses which are rented out to visitors, rather than for replacing small motels and beach cottages which were more usual in the past.

RIVERS IN FLOOD

water inundating normally dry land as river levels rise after heavy rainfall
or as a result of melting snow

River Trent, Midlands, UK

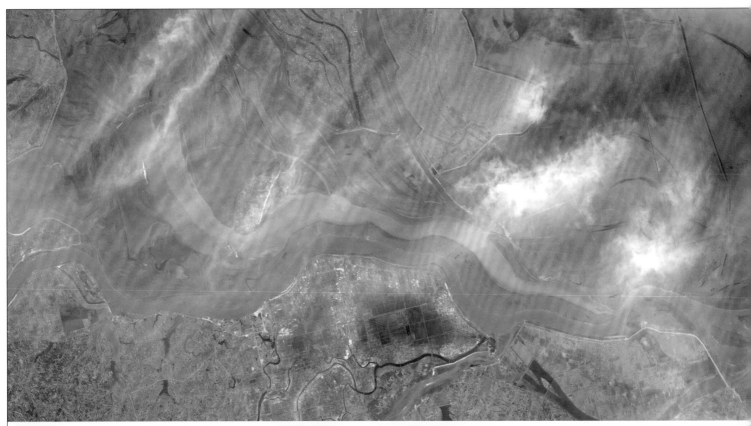

DONGTING HU, YANGTZE RIVER, CHINA 19 MARCH 2002 AND 2 SEPTEMBER 2002

Dongting Hu is a lake on the Yangtze river. It is the second largest freshwater lake in China, but is only approximately 45 per cent of its size of 150 years ago when it covered 6200 sq km (2394 sq miles). Land reclamation has reduced its size, but this activity was stopped in 1981. However, the high sediment load in the Yangtze continues to be a huge problem, silting up the lake.

As approximately 40 per cent of the Yangtze river water flows through the lake, when in August 2002 a large flood crest surged down the river inundating the lake area, as seen in the lower image it was potentially catastrophic for the local people. Fortunately, the embankments made by the locals held up, but in the past flood waters have inundated the land around the lake.

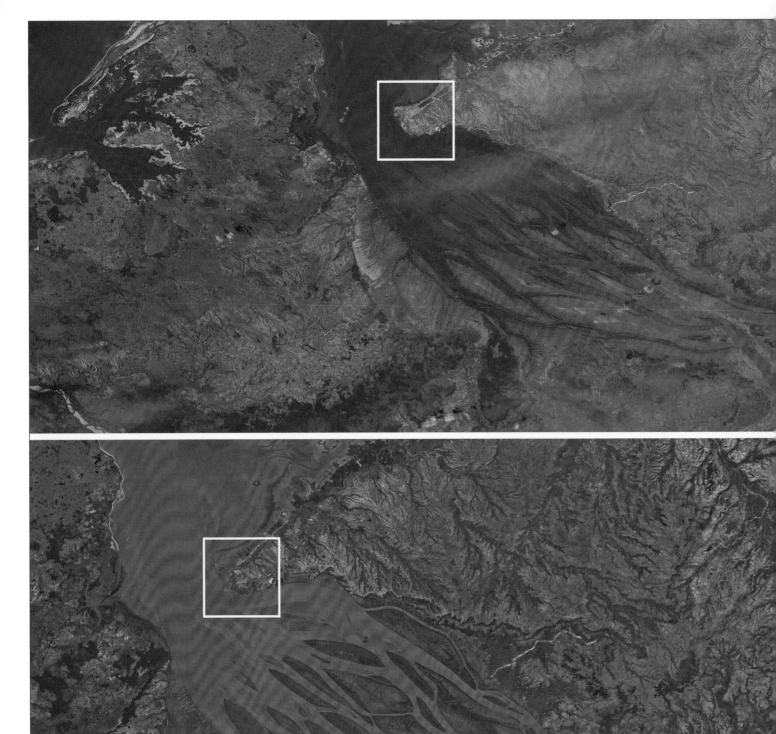

BETSIBOKA RIVER, MADAGASCAR 4 SEPTEMBER 2003 AND 25 MARCH 2004

Catastrophic erosion in northwestern Madagascar has resulted from the removal of native forest for timber. The top image shows normal river levels but below that the widespread flooding and massive red sediment plume as a result of tropical cyclone Gafilo, which hit northern Madagascar on 7 and 8 March 2004 can be seen. Not only is the soil upstream eroding but the sediment is silting up the estuary causing further problems.

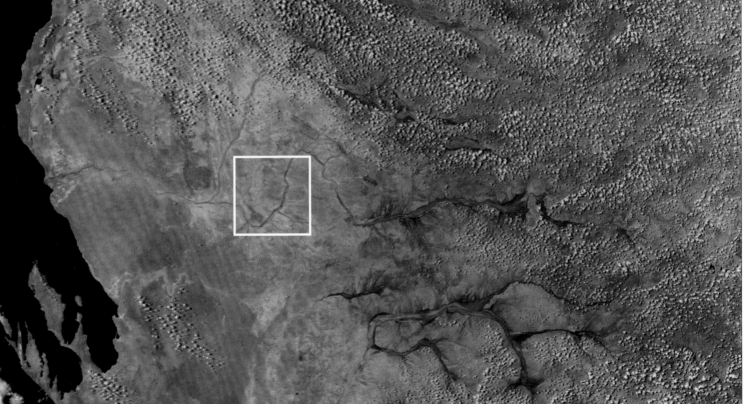

FLOODING IN WESTERN AUSTRALIA   20 FEBRUARY 2006 AND 2 MARCH 2006

A typical late summer season view of Western Australia can be seen in the top image, but on 1 March 2006 cyclone Emma hit and the ground was deluged with heavy rain. This triggered widespread flooding in the Murchison and Gascoyne river basins as seen in the bottom image. Vegetation has flourished in this wet period, making the flooded rivers stand out clearly.

BEWDLEY, WORCESTERSHIRE, UK 2000 AND FEBRUARY 2004

Until relatively recently, whenever the river Severn burst its banks and flooded, Bewdley suffered badly, as can be seen in the top image. However, flood defences have now been installed. During a flood a defence wall is now raised, keeping the buildings behind safe.

KLOSTER WELTENBURG, BAVARIA, GERMANY   31 JULY 1999 AND 25 AUGUST 2005

Kloster Weltenburg, a normally serene Benedictine monastery on the banks of the Danube, dates back to AD 600. There has been a brewery on the site since 1050 and it is a popular tourist destination. In August 2005 the river rose by 7 m (24 feet), flooding the monastery buildings, but not the brewery.

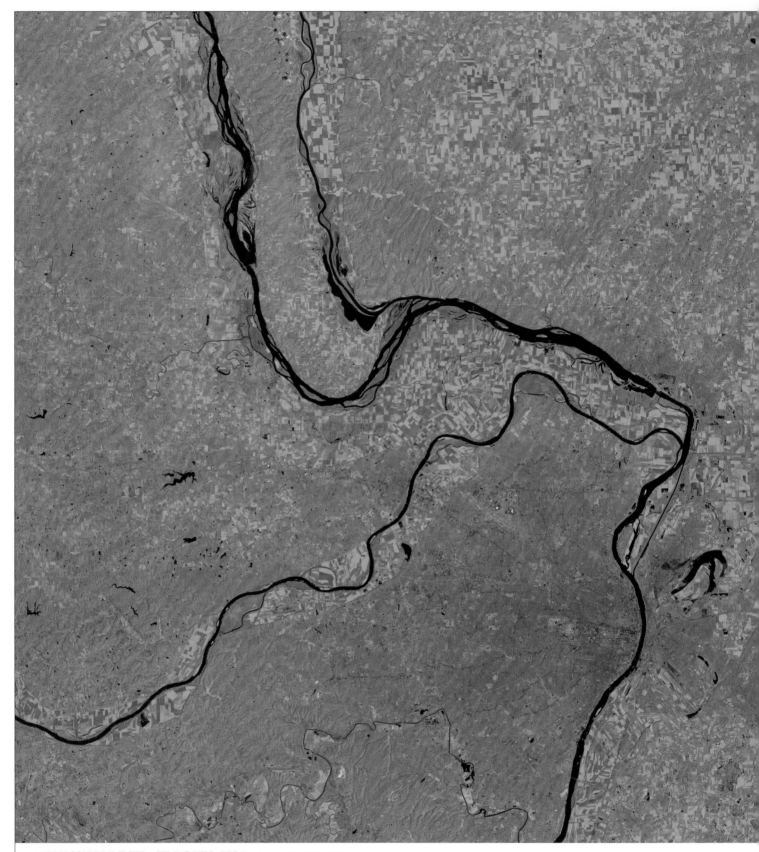

MISSISSIPPI RIVER, ST LOUIS, USA 14 AUGUST 1991

In the area around St Louis, the Mississippi, Missouri and Illinois rivers all meet. The land cover along the river banks has been changed from natural vegetation to agricultural land or is built up. This means that the wetlands which can absorb large amounts of water and release it slowly over time are missing, replaced by levees, canals and dams.

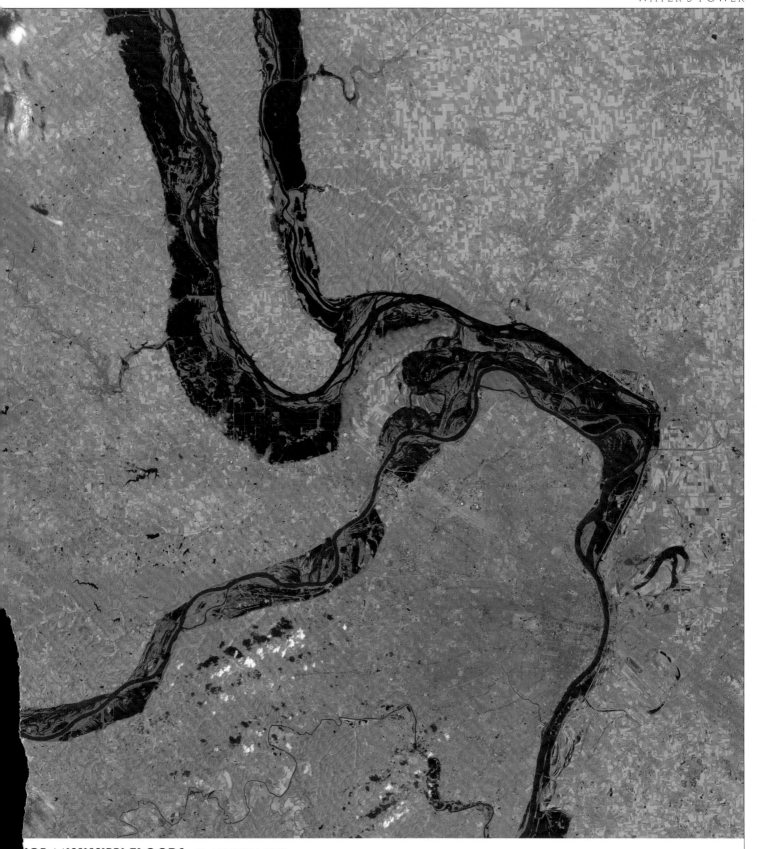

JOR MISSISSIPPI FLOODS 19 AUGUST 1993

y 1993 the upper Mississippi drainage basin received up to twice the average
, often during very intense storms. Floods overwhelmed the water control
res in the basin leading to the biggest flood ever recorded in the area.

In St Louis the Mississippi stayed above flood stage from 1 April until 30 September.
In this August image the pink areas show exposed soil as the water gradually retreats.

Index

ACKNOWLEDGEMENTS
FRAGILE EARTH

Pages 8–15 EARTHQUAKES
8–9
Alamy/Pacific Press Service/Masanori Kobayashi
10-11
Getty Images/Pictorial Parade/Justin Sullivan
12
Earl and Nazima Kowall/CORBIS
13
Ryan Pyle/CORBIS
14
U.S. Coast Guard photo by Petty Officer 2nd Class Sondra-Kay Kneen.
15
Satellite image courtesy of GeoEye
15 inset top
M_Eriksson
15 inset bottom
United Nations Development Programme

Pages 16–23 VOLCANOES
16–17
Used with kind permission of Sverrir Þorolfsson
18
USGS/D.A. Swanson
19 top
USGS/Cascades Volcano Observatory/Jim Nieland, U.S. Forest Service
19 bottom
USGS/Cascades Volcano Observatory/Lyn Topinka
20 top
POPPERFOTO/Getty
20 bottom
© CORBIS
21 top
FLPA/Alamy
21 bottom
ARCTIC IMAGES/Alamy
22
BERNHARD EDMAIER/SCIENCE PHOTO LIBRARY
23
NASA/Earth Observatory

Pages 24–29 TSUNAMI
24–25
Shutterstock/SURABKY
26–27
IKONOS images © CRISP 2004
28–29
IKONOS images © CRISP 2004

Pages 30–37 LANDSLIDES
30–31
Shutterstock/Jeffrey Liao
32
Earth Observatory/Space Imaging
33
NASA image created by Jesse Allen, using data provided courtesy of GSFC/METI/ERSDAC/JAROS, and the U.S./Japan ASTER Science Team
34 top
PA/PA/EMPICS
34 bottom
John Giles/PA/EMPICS
35 top
Peter Schneider/AP/EMPICS
35 bottom
Hans Rudolf Burgener/Greenpeace
36
NASA/Earth Observatory
37
© BELCASTRO ANTONIETTA/epa/Corbis

Pages 38–43 TROPICAL STORMS
38–39
Shutterstock/Robert Ranson
40–41
IKONOS images courtesy of GeoEye
42–43
NASA/Earth Observatory

Pages 44–47 Tornadoes
44–45
Shutterstock/Photography Perspectives – Jeff Smith
46–47
Michel Gunther/Still Pictures

Pages 48–53 DUSTSTORMS
48–49
Shutterstock/André Klaassen
50
Shutterstock/Amy Nichole Harris
51
Lou Linwei/Alamy
52–53
NOAA/Department of Commerce

Pages 54–61 SNOW
54–55
Shutterstock/Jason Maehl
56–57
MODIS/NASA

58–59
NASA/GSFC
60–61
NASA/GSFC

Pages 62–71 POLAR ICE
62–63
Shutterstock/Armin Rose
64–65
MODIS/NASA
66–67
MODIS/NASA
68–69
MODIS/NASA
70
Bryan & Cherry Alexander Photography
71
Tony A. Weyiouanna Sr. Kawerak Transportation Program

Pages 72–89 SHRINKING GLACIERS
72–73
Shutterstock/javarman
74–75
Lonnie G. Thompson, The Byrd Polar Research Institute, Ohio State University
76
NSIDC/William O. Field
77
NSIDC/Bruce F. Molina
78–79
NSIDC/Bruce F. Molina
80–81
NASA/ Earth Observatory/ASTER data
82 left
T.J. Hileman, courtesy of Glacier National Park Archives
82 right
Lindsey Bengtson/USGS
83 top
E.C. Stebinger, courtesy of Glacier National Park Archives
83 bottom
Lisa McKeon/USGS
84
NASA/Earth Observatory
85 top
Archivo Museo Salesiano
85 bottom
Daniel Beltra/Greenpeace
86
NASA images created by Jesse Allen, Earth Observatory, using data provided courtesy of NASA/GSFC/METI/ERSDAC/JAROS, and the U.S./Japan ASTER Science Team.
87 top
Shutterstock/Peter Wolinga
87 bottom
Shutterstock/tomtsya
88
NASA/GSFC/METI/ERSDAC/JAROS, and U.S./Japan ASTER Science Team
89
Shutterstock/Elisabeth Holm

Pages 90–99 RISING SEA LEVELS
90–91
Shutterstock/Antonio S.
92–93
Gary Braasch
94
IKONOS image courtesy of GeoEye
95 top
Shahee Ilyas
95 bottom
Shutterstock/paokun
96–97
US Geological Survey Center for Coastal Geology
98
Sutterstock/Eugene Moglinikov
99
Shutterstock/phhotooiasson

Pages 100–107 DEFORESTATION
100–101
Shutterstock/Dhoxax
102–103
Images reproduced by kind permission of UNEP
104–105
Images reproduced by kind permission of UNEP
106–107
NASA/Earth Observatory

Pages 108–113 ADVANCING DESERTS
108–109
Shutterstock/Pichugin Dmitry
110–111
Voltchev/UNEP/Still Pictures
112
© Nic Bothma/epa/CORBIS
113
Mark Henley/Panos

Pages 114–121 DROUGHT AND FIRE
114–115
Altitude/Still Pictures
116–117
NASA/Earth Observatory
118
© Reuters/CORBIS
119
Mark Edwards/Still Pictures
120–121
NASA/Earth Observatory

Pages 122–135 DRYING LAKES AND RIVERS
122–123
Shutterstock/A. Vogler
124–125
Image reproduced by kind permission of UNEP
126
USGS, EROS Data Center, Sioux Falls, SD; 2005 MODIS/NASA
127
MODIS/NASA
128–129
NASA/Earth Observatory
130–131
Courtesy of John Dohrenwend
132–133
NASA/Earth Observatory
134
Image State/Alamy
135
© 2006 Shunya

Pages 136–145 CHANGING COASTLINES
136–137
Shutterstock/Angela Crowley
138
Dylan Banarse/Bettina Furnee; www.ifever.org.uk
139
Aerofilms
139
Patricia & Angus Macdonald, Aerographica
140 top
David Woodfall/Woodfall Wild Images
140 bottom
Stacey Peak Media
141
US Geological Survey Center for Coastal Geology
142–143
© Parks Victoria/Handout/Reuters/CORBIS
144–145
Image reproduced by kind permission of UNEP
146–147
Gary Braasch

Pages 148–157 RIVERS IN FLOOD
148–149
© Skyscan/Corbis
150–151
NASA and U.S./Japan ASTER Science Team
152
NASA
153
NASA/Earth Observatory/MODIS data
154 top
Paul Glendell/Alamy
154 bottom
Steve Sant/Alamy
155 top
© Adam Woolfitt/CORBIS
155 bottom
Alexander Ruesche/DPA/EMPICS
156–157
NASA/Earth Observatory/Landsat data

We would like to acknowledge the assistance of :
The United Nations Environment Programme (www.na.unep.net) in providing selected images from One Planet Many People – Atlas of Our Changing Environment, UNEP, 2005 (www.earthprint.com).

Pages 92–93, 146–147 Gary Braasch (worldviewofglobalwarming.org) for images from the book Earth Under Fire: How Global Warming is Changing the World (University of California Press, 2007).

GeoEye www.geoeye.com
NASA earthobservatory.nasa.gov
NASA rapidfire.sci.gsfc.nasa.gov
NASA asterweb.jpl.nasa.gov/index.asp
United States Geological Survey www.usgs.gov